C000002358

On T
Grass
When I
Arrive

An Anthology of New Writing from Northern
Ireland on Place, Home, and Belonging

Edited with an Introduction by
Leon Litvack

GUILDHALL PRESS

Published in 2016 by
Guildhall Press
Ráth Mór Centre
Bligh's Lane
Derry BT48 0LZ
T: (028) 7136 4413
info@ghpress.com www.ghpress.com

Cover image: Naomi Litvack, *Wild Road* (2014). Oil on board, 29x21cm

Copyright © Leon Litvack and the contributing authors

ISBN 978 1 911053 13 2

Supported by the National Lottery through the Big Lottery Fund

A CIP record for this book is available from the British Library.

The authors assert their moral rights in this work in accordance with the
Copyright, Designs and Patents Act 1998.

CONTENTS

PROSE

ACKNOWLEDGEMENTS

I would like to thank the contributors to this volume, most of whom were participants in the project entitled 'Writing and Community: Ideas of Place', funded by the Big Lottery, through its Culture for All programme, and the Arts Council of Northern Ireland. The idea behind this initiative was to explore ideas about home, place, origins, identity and community, through facilitated creative writing workshops. There was, it was felt, a profound need for the citizens of Northern Ireland to be aware not only of their sense of rootedness to home and place, but also of mobility, openness, and displacement, which are all features of our modern society. Some of the contributors were experienced creative writers; others were relative novices. The work of project participants was encouraged and, in some cases, edited by the expert facilitators who conducted the workshops: Jan Carson, Sharon Dempsey, Moyra Donaldson, Jo Egan, Caroline Healy, Fionnuala Kennedy, Kiyan Khosravi, Chelley McClear, Bernie McGill, Martelle McPartland, and Erika Meitner. I have them to thank for encouraging the writers to produce and rework their insightful, carefully crafted efforts.

The project could not have been completed without the invaluable assistance of my Administrator, Paul Maddern. He organised the workshop sessions and the performance event at the Crescent Arts Centre, and ensured that everything accorded with our plan. Paul's input was not only organisational, but also intellectual: he helped me to develop the scope for the post-show discussion on the meaning of place in Northern Irish writing, and he also assisted in selecting material for the anthology. It is a testament to his own creative efficacy that several of his own poems have been included.

Editors need time to assemble their selected contributions into a coherent whole, and if the work is carried out in inspiring surroundings, the resulting volume is, hopefully, the better for it. With this in mind, I would like to thank my dear friends, old and new, at the University of New Brunswick. My first academic visit to Fredericton was in March 2014, to deliver the W.C. Desmond Pacey Memorial Lecture on Titanic. I returned in the summer of 2015, as the Fredrik and Catherine Eaton Research Fellow. It was during that latter, glorious sojourn that the bulk of the editing of this anthology was carried out. I enjoyed many fruitful discussions with colleagues in the Department of English and in the Milton F. Gregg Centre for the Study of War and Society. For countless kindnesses I'd like to thank Mark Jarman, Mary Rimmer, Clarissa Hurley, Adrian Tronson, Ross Leckie, Kathryn Taglia, Marc Milner, Jen Andrews, Janet Noiles, Theresa Keenan, Gwen Davies, Richard Hornsby, Joanne Wright, and Edie Snook. I'd also like to thank my old Trinity friends John Ball and Randall Martin, with whom old ties were renewed and strengthened. We also had a number of intrepid Ontario visitors to New Brunswick during our stay: Chuck and Wendy, Allen and Harriet, and Wayne and Brenda. We will treasure the memories of the good times we shared!

Finally, I owe a debt of gratitude to my own institution, Queen's University Belfast, and my dear colleague, Paul Simpson, for nominating me for the Eaton Fellowship. The intimate and multiple connections between Northern Ireland and Canada continue to exercise a powerful influence on me, and the name of Eaton plays no small part in that story.

Leon Litvack

The following authors have provided pieces previously published elsewhere:

CIARAN CARSON. 'Turn Again' from *Belfast Confetti* (1989), by kind permission of the author and The Gallery Press.

MOYRA DONALDSON. 'Dunluce Avenue' from *Miracle Fruit* (2010), by kind permission of the author and Lagan Press; 'Greba Cras' and 'Movilla Cemetery' from *The Goose Tree* (2014), by kind permission of the author and Liberties Press.

ALAN GILLIS. 'The Lights' from *Hawks and Doves* (2007), by kind permission of the author and The Gallery Press.

PAUL MADDERN. 'Harbour', 'Lines at Lacken Mill', and 'Postamble' from *The Beachcomber's Report* (2010), by kind permission of the author and Templar Poetry.

ERIKA MEITNER. 'Conflict Tourism', from *The Rumpus*, 20 April 2015, by kind permission of the author; 'Non-Lieux, on the Academy of American Poets Poem-A-Day website, 30 September 2014, by kind permission of the author.

INTRODUCTION
Leon Litvack

In 2006 Seamus Heaney published *District and Circle*, a collection which featured the poem 'The Blackbird of Glanmore'; it opens with these lines:

> On the grass when I arrive,
> Filling the stillness with life,
> But ready to scare off
> At the very first wrong move.
> In the ivy when I leave.

> It's you, blackbird, I love.[1]

The speaker (who may be associated with Heaney himself) comes home from his first term at college, parks the car, and finds a blackbird sitting on the ground by the house. He makes a variety of comments about the creature, remarking on its skittishness, its playful bounding through the yard, its powers of observation, and its ready engagement with its recently arrived observer. It is a deeply personal poem, and in its interplay between long and short stanzas it covers a range of concerns; foremost among them are the memories of the poet's brother Christopher, who died in a road accident in 1952 (and beside whom

---

1 *District and Circle* (London: Faber & Faber, 2006), p. 75.

Heaney was buried in 2013).[2] The blackbird serves as a harbinger of death, but also as a testament to life: the speaker not only remarks that 'yon bird' sat on the ridge of the roof for weeks after the tragedy, but he also comes to associate himself with the creature, and is endowed with a 'bird's eye view' of himself, as he recalls time spent with his brother, when 'talkback' and 'stand-offish comeback' were part of the ordinary activities in which they engaged.[3]

There is clear attachment to 'home' in the poem; it is a place revisited, familiar yet changing as time passes. Heaney's early associations with the place are coloured by his brother's tragic death; but when he revisits the place he sees it differently: it has become a 'house of life'. 'The Blackbird of Glanmore' demonstrates that we can have a variety of responses to 'home' or 'place' – sometimes within the same work of art. Our feelings may lie deep within us, and may require some unpacking. Elmer Kennedy Andrews explores Heaney's own evocative attitudes:

For Heaney, place is the primal and primary determinant – the ground – of identity for both self and community, especially in times of disturbance, and in a context of historical colonialism and encroaching modernity. . . [he] seeks an alternative

---

2 Greg Harkin, 'Seamus Heaney: Bellaghy's famous son will rest beside his little brother', *Belfast Telegraph*, 31 August 2013.
3 *District and Circle*, p. 76.

in the assumed continuity of place, "authentic" community and submerged Gaelic/pagan folk culture in his rural "first world".[4]

Heaney has a clear idea about where he locates his centre – what he calls, in an early autobiographical essay, his *omphalos*.[5] His ideas about 'place' are rather particular to the geographies and landscapes of his experience; he seeks to develop a confidence in his poetic settings, thus communicating a vision of relationship and belonging which resonates with his readers.

Heaney expands on some of these ideas in his essay entitled 'The Sense of Place', most of which is taken up with an assessment of the work of Patrick Kavanagh and John Montague, in terms of their attachment to the land. He emphasises, for example, the 'profound importance of the parochial' for Kavanagh, and the poet's attendance at the 'intimate hedge-school'.[6] He also offers some general observations on the two primary ways in which place is known and cherished: the 'lived, illiterate and unconscious' way, and the 'learned, literate and conscious' way. It is the tension between these, he says, that inspires the poetry under discussion.[7] Heaney also observes that the imagination

4 Elmer Kennedy-Andrews, *Writing Home: Poetry and Place in Northern Ireland, 1968-2008* (Cambridge: D.S. Brewer, 2008), pp. 83-4.

5 Seamus Heaney, 'Mossbawn', in *Preoccupations: Selected Prose 1968-1978* (London: Faber & Faber, 1980), p. 17.

6 'The Sense of Place', in *Preoccupations*, p. 137.

7 'The Sense of Place', p. 131.

is nourished by both the 'geographical country' and the 'country of the mind' in our conception of our own sense of place, and our sense of ourselves as inhabitants.[8] The use of the language of the geographer is significant, for it is in this area of scholarly inquiry that some of the most interesting debates have emerged concerning ideas of place, space, and home.

The conception of place is, of course, an important way for human beings to know and understand the world. We form an adherence to place, and we invest it with meaning. In the 1970s humanistic geographers explored the mechanisms by which we become attached to place; they used a phenomenological approach – that is, they took as their starting point the 'phenomena of the lived-world of immediate experience', and then sought to 'clarify these in a rigorous way by careful observation and description'.[9] Among the most influential of these is the Chinese-American scholar Yi-Fu Tuan, who published two key texts: *Topophilia* (1974), and *Space and Place* (1977). In *Topophilia* (which Tuan characterises not merely as human love of place, but also as a 'neologism' which broadly includes 'all of the human being's affective ties with the material environment')[10] he examines

---

8 'The Sense of Place', p. 132.
9 Edward Relph, *Place and Placelessness* (London: Pion, 1976), p. i. See also Tim Cresswell, *Place: A Short Introduction* (Oxford: Blackwell, 2004), p. 23, where he notes that the central concern of phenomenology is 'intentionality', or the 'aboutness' of human consciousness.
10 Yi-Fu Tuan, *Topophilia: A Study of Environmental Perception, Attitudes, and Values* (Englewood Cliffs: Prentice-Hall, 1974), pp. 92, 93.

many aspects of the 'affective bond between people and place or setting'.[11] He carefully synthesizes his material, drawing in religion, philosophy, anthropology, history, psychology, aesthetics, and biology, in order to explore why human beings vary in the perceptions, attitudes, and values they apply to their psychosocial worlds. He identifies sources of universality (such as human stereoscopic vision, our possession of five senses, and our tendency towards ethnocentrism), as well as sources of variation (visual acuity, culture, individual biography, and world view), which affect human perception of place. In this wide-ranging text, one must wait until the conclusion to learn how Tuan draws the various strands together. He observes that human beings are simultaneously biological organisms, social beings, and unique individuals, and while we are 'well-equipped biologically to register a vast array of environmental stimuli', we actually sense very little, because 'culture and environment largely determine which of the senses are favored'.[12] Tuan then notes that 'the group, expressing and enforcing the cultural standards of society, affects strongly the perception, attitude, and environmental value of its members'. Thus culture influences perception 'to the degree that people will see things that do not exist: it can cause group hallucination'.[13]

Tuan then reflects on what appeals to people when

11 *Topophilia*, p. 4.
12 *Topophilia*, p. 245.
13 *Topophilia*, p. 246.

they contemplate ideal places from which they derive pleasure. He writes:

> Certain natural environments have figured prominently in humanity's dreams of the ideal world: they are the forest, the seashore, the valley, and the island. The furnishing of an ideal world is a matter of removing the defects of the real one. Geography necessarily provides the content of topophilic sentiment. Paradises have a certain family likeness because all the excesses of geography (too hot or too cold, too wet or too dry) are removed. In all of them, plants and animals useful and friendly to [humankind] abound.

Such views – despite the fact that they are widely held – are, Tuan asserts, false; he adds:

> Statistics giving us the number of people who visit the National Parks or buy summer homes are better measures of fashion and the state of the economy than of people's real sentiments concerning nature.[14]

Yet we must recognise that countless writers, and the public at large, crave such visions of perfection.[15] If

---

14 *Topophilia*, p. 247.
15 Kennedy-Andrews notes that Heaney's 'closed' version of Irishness, implicit in his image of *omphalos,* assumes that 'the further you move

an inexperienced writer is asked to pen a piece about a physical setting, there is a likelihood that he/she will express visual pleasure and sensual delight, and a perceptual bias mediated by culture. Tuan observes that human beings have continually searched for the ideal environment. He asserts:

> How it looks varies from one culture to another but in essence it seems to draw on two antipodal images: the garden of innocence and the cosmos. The fruits of the earth provide security as also does the harmony of the stars which offers, in addition, grandeur, so we move from one to the other: from the shade under the baobab to the magic circle under heaven; from home to public square, from suburb to city; from seaside holiday to the enjoyment of the sophisticated arts, seeking for a point of equilibrium that is not of this world.[16]

These idealized notions are significant, and should not be dismissed out of hand. Many writers who conjure up perfect, Edenic images of place or home often do so because of an intense emotional investment in locations

---

from origins the more tenuous and unstable your identity becomes' (*Writing Home*, p. 14). Kennedy-Andrews goes on to demonstrate that in the more recent work of Northern Irish writers like Paul Muldoon, Ciaran Carson, Medbh McGuckian and others, there is a 'deterritorialising' effect: a 'loosening of the fixed, bounded, rooted conceptions of home and identity' (p. 15).

16 *Topophilia*, 248.

where they have felt safety, security, and a passionate sense of belonging.

In Tuan's other influential work, *Space and Place*, he seeks to humanise discussions about place, because, he says, experiential data is often ignored by planners, housing authorities, social scientists, and others who are primarily concerned with practical issues. He observes:

> Much of human experience is difficult to articulate. . . and we are far from finding devices that measure satisfactorily the quality of a feeling or aesthetic response. What we cannot say in acceptable scientific language we tend to deny or forget.[17]

In order to emphasise the value of 'experience' – a key term for Tuan[18] – he explores such topics as children's attitudes to space and place (which for them are more matter-of-fact, and linked to activity rather than knowledge or memory),[19] as well as issues of the body, personal relations and spatial values (in which he explains, with the aid of some helpful diagrams, that human beings impose a schema on space, privileging the centre, as well as the vertical axis, so that higher is more desirable).[20] Tuan also considers issues of time in space, noting that humans are 'biased in favor of the

17 Yi-Fu Tuan, *Space and Place: The Perspective of Experience* (Minneapolis: University of Minnesota Press, 1977), p. 200.
18 *Space and Place*, p. 7.
19 *Space and Place*, pp. 32-3.
20 *Space and Place*, pp. 35-7.

future', so that for them time becomes directional, and indeed asymmetrical: 'one's back is to the past, one's face to the future'. 'Living', he says, 'is a perpetual stepping forward into light and abandoning what is behind one's back'.[21] When he comes to consider time and place, he notes that there is a distinction to be drawn between space and place; he observes: 'If we think of space as that which allows movement, then place is pause; each pause in movement makes it possible for location to be transformed into place.[22] Space is a rather abstract concept: it is area and volume; we tend to think, for instance, of outer space.[23] Place, on the other hand, is a more concrete, 'static' concept: it takes people time to form an attachment to, or 'feel' of a place, which is made up of 'experiences, mostly fleeting and undramatic, repeated day after day and over the span of years'; it is, Tuan says, 'a unique blend of sights, sounds, and smells, a unique harmony of natural and artificial rhythms.[24]

In a chapter entitled 'Attachment to Homeland', Tuan explores the idea of rootedness to a place. He posits that 'Human groups. . . tend to regard their own homeland as the centre of the world. A people who believe they are at the centre claim, implicitly, the ineluctable worth of their location'.[25] 'Such a conception of place', he

---

21 *Space and Place*, pp. 132, 135.

22 *Space and Place*, p. 6.

23 See Creswell, p. 9.

24 *Space and Place*, pp. 179, 183-4.

25 *Space and Place*, p. 149. For an extended analysis by Tuan of this idea see 'Rootedness versus Sense of Place', *Landscape* 24 (1980): 3-8.

adds, 'ought to give it supreme value; to abandon it would be hard to imagine'. Should destruction of this place occur, we ought to think that the people would be devastated, and unable to recover; yet this does not necessarily happen because, Tuan reasons,

> Human beings have strong recuperative powers. Cosmic views can be adjusted to suit new circumstances. With the destruction of one "center of the world," another can be built next to it, or in another location, and it in turn can become the center of the world. "Center" is not a particular point on the earth's surface; it is a concept in mythic thought rather than a deeply felt value bound to unique events and locality.[26]

In thinking about these ideas Tuan never becomes sentimental or trite; he is able to analyse how people feel about place and space in a way that is refreshing and convincing – at least for a literary scholar. His ultimate point is that as human beings, we develop multi-perceptional, intricately attitudinal stances towards concepts that seem so simple, that we rarely think to unpack them to get at their essence, but instead surround them with a host of contestible notions about literary tradition, historical circumstances, political positionings, religious controversies, and other circumstances which do not speak to the essence of what human beings experience.

---

26 *Space and Time*, pp. 149-50.

Another humanistic geographer who explores what he considers universally applicable ideas about place is Edward Relph, who in 1976 published a short, widely referenced study entitled *Place and Placelessness*. While acknowledging the congruence of Tuan's work with his own,[27] Relph places heightened significance on the conception of place as a 'philosophical endeavour'.[28] Using ideas gleaned from the pronouncements of Martin Heidegger, in *Unterwegs zur Sprache* (published in English in 1971 as *Poetry, Language, Thought*), he moves beyond the notion of place as location, and links it more intimately to our consciousness and what defines us as human beings:

> The basic meaning of place, its essence, does not. . . come from locations, nor from the trivial functions that places serve, nor from the community that occupies it, nor from superficial and mundane experiences – though these are all common and perhaps necessary aspects of places. The essence of place lies in the largely unselfconscious intentionality that defines places as profound centres of human existence.[29]

To be human, then, is to have an intimate, indissoluble link with place. Relph explores the depths of this

---

27 *Place and Placelessness*, p. 2.

28 Cresswell, p. 22.

29 *Place and Placelessness*, p. 43.

association in various ways in his study. While acknowledging that place may be sensed in a 'chiaroscuro of setting, landscape, ritual, routine, other people, personal experiences, care and concern for home, and in the context of other places',[30] he provides considerations of such concepts as 'insideness', which he usefully subdivides into the existential, incidental, vicarious, behavioural, and the empathetic.[31] The last of these, posits Relph, is the deepest, and leads the individual to an understanding of the identity of a place;[32] he explains:

> Empathetic insideness demands a willingness to be open to significances of a place, to feel it, to know and respect its symbols – much as a person might experience a holy place as sacred without necessarily believing in that particular religion. . . . To be inside a place empathetically is to understand that place as rich in meaning, and hence to identify with it, for these meanings are not only linked to the experiences and symbols of those whose place it is, but also stem from one's own experiences.[33]

What has been offered about Relph's work thus far might make it appear naïve, in light of the many

---

30 *Place and Placelessness*, p. 29.

31 *Place and Placelessness*, pp. 49-55.

32 Relph defines the identity of place as 'the very basis of our experience of *this* place as opposed to any other' (p. 62).

33 *Place and Placelessness*, pp. 54-5.

developments in place theory which have occurred since the 1970s; but Relph also acknowledges and explores the inverse of place – that is, placelessness, as a growing reality. It is driven, he argues, by an inauthentic attitude to place, which is merely 'socially convenient and acceptable – an uncritically accepted stereotype, an intellectual or aesthetic fashion that can be adopted without real involvement'.[34] In this evolution of attitudes, Relph notes, 'home' has become a 'marketable, exchangeable, and sentimentalized good', because of the fascination with 'kitsch': in this changed relationship between human beings and the material world, 'objects are created and produced solely for consumption by a mass public', thus resulting in 'mediocrity' and 'phoniness' rather than 'excellence' and 'honesty'.[35] Relph adds that an 'inauthentic' attitude towards place develops as a result of the dominance of 'mass communications, mass culture, big business, powerful central authority, and the economic system which embraces all these'.[36] He gives examples of the adverse consequences of these trends, if allowed to proceed unchecked: they result, he believes, in 'synthetic landscapes and pseudo-places', the creation of 'subtopias' or the 'Disneyfication' of place.[37] Relph

---

34 *Place and Placelessness*, p. 82.

35 *Place and Placelessness*, pp. 83, 82.

36 *Place and Placelessness*, p. 90.

37 *Place and Placelessness*, pp. 93, 105, 95-6. 'Subtopia' is a term used by Relph to describe an urban fringe area, or subdivision (housing development), or a commercial development, consisting of 'a set of apparently randomly located points and areas, each of which serves a single purpose

concludes his study with a stark choice for us:

> A deep human need exists for association with significant places. If we choose to ignore that need, and to allow the forces of placelessness to continue unchallenged, then the future can only hold an environment in which places simply do not matter. If, on the other hand, we choose to respond to that need and to transcend placelessness, then the potential exists for the development of an environment in which places are for [humankind], reflecting and enhancing the variety of human experience.[38]

Tuan and Relph laid down an important foundation for the study of place, and they construct the terms of their arguments in such a way as to explain – helpfully – how human beings experience the world; yet the observations of these humanistic geographers rely on relatively fixed and finite ideas about place. Other, more recent, critics have challenged such notions; Allan Pred, for example, believes that humanistic geographers 'conceive of place as an inert, experienced scene'. He argues instead for a conceptualization of place as never finished, and always in process; place is, he says, 'a constantly becoming human product'.[39]

and each of which is isolated from its setting, linked only by roads which are themselves isolated from the surrounding townscape' (p. 109).
38 *Place and Placelessness*, p. 147.
39 Allan Pred, 'Place as Historically Contingent Process: Structuration and the Time-Geography of Becoming Places', *Annals of the Association of*

Through the employment of structuration theory,[40] he demonstrates how the 'establishment, reproduction, and transformation of power relations' contributes to the becoming of place, so that, for example, when economic and state institutions come into contact with the local and the everyday, there is a shift in the 'humanly made elements of place'.[41] For Pred, then, place is alive with possibilities, in terms of how it is affected by human structures and interactions.

More recent critics have, then, reconceived place as fluid, open, and progressive. The British feminist and cultural geographer Doreen Massey, in her seminal essay 'A Global Sense of Place', takes issue with 'reactionary' notions of place, because they give rise to 'certain forms of nationalism, sentimentalized recovering of sanitized "heritages", and outright antagonism to newcomers and "outsiders"'. She asks: 'Can't we rethink our sense of place? Is it not possible for a sense of place to be progressive; not self-enclosing and defensive, but outward-looking? A sense of place which is adequate to this era of time-space compression?'[42] For Massey, our increasing drive

American Geography 74.2 (1984): 279.

40 A social theory which links behaviour and structure, through an examination of the creation and perpetuation of social systems. See Anthony Giddens, *The Constitution of Society: Outline of the Theory of Structuration* (Cambridge: Polity Press, 1984).

41 Pred, pp. 291, 282. For a fuller explication see Cresswell, p. 35.

42 Doreen Massey, 'A Global Sense of Place', in *Space, Place and Gender* (Cambridge: Polity Press, 1994), p. 147. 'Time-space compression' (a key phrase for Massey) refers to 'movement and communication across space', and the 'geographical stretching-out of social relations'; it results, she says,

towards globalisation in many areas of our lives has a profound and far-reaching effect on 'power-geometry' – that is, not only 'who moves and who doesn't', but also 'power in relation *to* the flows and the movement'.[43] She discusses the changes brought about by immigration to her local shopping area in north-west London, Kilburn High Road, in order to demonstrate how places can be thought of as 'articulated moments in networks of social relations and understandings'; such considerations, she argues, allow a place to appear 'extroverted', and imbued with a 'consciousness of its links with the wider world, which integrates in a positive way the global and the local'.[44] If such an alternative conception is adopted, Massey believes that place may be seen as 'constructed out of a particular constellation of social relations, meeting together at a particular locus'.[45] This opening out of the construction of place is a useful development, and may be seen, in some ways, as diametrically opposed to the notions developed by Tuan and Relph.[46]

In another essay in her volume *Space, Place and Gender*, Massey considers the question of 'home', in an age when so many people in the world are experiencing dislocation, fragmentation, and disorientation. She expresses concern that there is 'all too much evidence

from 'the actions of capital' and 'its currently increasing internationalization' (p. 147).
43 'A Global Sense of Place', p. 149; emphasis original.
44 'A Global Sense of Place', p. 155.
45 'A Global Sense of Place', p. 154.
46 See Cresswell, p. 74.

of the emergence of disquieting forms of place-bound loyalties', as well as 'burgeoning exclusive localisms' on the right wing of the political spectrum.[47] These observations are as relevant today as they were when Massey was writing in the early 1990s; but such disruptions, with the associated movement of people, open up new possibilities for how we might think about home – and indeed, in her opinion, how it always should have been imagined. She notes:

> A large component of the identity of that place called home derived precisely from the fact that it had always in one way or another been open: constructed out of movement, communication, social relations which always stretched beyond it.[48]

It is useful to think of the identity of a place as 'provisional' or 'open to contestation', because it challenges long-held notions about the static nature of home and belonging.[49]

If these pronouncements are interpreted positively, there emerges an openness about home and its parameters; yet questions about who holds power and authority intrude into the debate. Massey notes that 'There is. . . an issue of whose identity we are referring to when we talk of a place called home and of the

47 'A Place Called Home?' in *Space, Place and Gender*, pp. 162-3.
48 'A Place Called Home?', pp. 170-1.
49 'A Place Called Home?', pp. 168, 169.

supports it may provide of stability, openness, and security'.[50] With this observation in mind, it is useful to consider the perspective of the black feminist critic bell hooks, who argues that home can function as a site of resistance. In her study entitled *Yearning*, she includes childhood reminiscences of visits to the house of her grandmother, who for the most part 'worked outside the home serving white folks, cleaning their houses, washing their clothes, tending their children'. She identifies a tension for such women between 'service outside one's home, family and kin network' and 'service (care and nurturance) within their own families and communities'. In this scenario the homeplace for these black women functions as 'the one site where one could freely confront the issue of humanization [*sic*], where one could resist'.[51] hooks does not, however, only recognise the 'subversive value of homeplace'; she recognises other – indeed broader – possibilities as well:

> Home is that place which enables and promotes varied and everchanging perspectives, a place where one discovers new ways of seeing reality, frontiers of difference. One confronts and accepts dispersal and fragmentation as part of the constructions of a new world order that reveals more fully where we are, who we can become.[52]

---

50 'A Place Called Home?', p. 167.
51 bell hooks, *Yearning: Race, Gender and Cultural Politics* (Boston: South End Press, 1990), p. 42.
52 hooks, *Yearning*, p. 148.

It is clear from the pronouncements of Massey and hooks that localised ideas about home and place are being edged out in favour of globalised ones. This is a fertile area of investigation, which has resulted in a fundamental reconsideration of place in our increasingly mobile, connected, and accelerated modes of existence.[53] Globalisation – with its capacity to engender hybrid or synchronous identities has, according to anthropologists Nigel Rapport and Andrew Dawson, 'made traditional conceptions of individuals as members of fixed and separate societies and cultures redundant'. Identity, they say, is a 'search, either physical or cognitive, and is conceived of in terms of fluidities – of time and space, time or space'. The result is that 'movement has become fundamental to modern identity', and what Rapport and Dawson call 'non-place' has become 'an essential component of everyday existence'.[54] Such views have important implications for scholars like the Colombian-American anthropologist Arturo Escobar, who examined strategies of localization among black communities in the Pacific rainforest region of Colombia. He builds on the work of Massey, and Rapport and Dawson, in order to ask whether it

---

53 For a useful consideration of mobility, in terms of the advent of so-called 'machinic complexes' in the nineteenth and twentieth centuries, see Nigel Thrift, 'Inhuman Geographies: Landscapes of Speed, Light and Power', in *Writing the Rural: Five Cultural Geographies* (London: Paul Chapman Publishing, 1994), pp. 191-238.

54 Nigel Rapport and Andrew Dawson (eds.), *Migrants of Identity: Perceptions of Home in a World of Movement* (Oxford and New York: Berg, 1998), pp. 3, 4, 6. See also pp. 22-4 on globalisation.

is possible to achieve a balance between the global and the local, by creating 'glocalities' – that is, 'cultural and spatial configurations that connect places with each other', so that everything can be perceived as global and local.[55] He believes in the 'continued vitality of place and place-making for culture, nature, and economy'[56] and suggests that subaltern social movements, like the test case he considers in Colombia, have the capacity to reconceive and reconstruct ideas of place. In this region (the so-called 'Pacífico biogeográfico') the Afro-Colombian inhabitants have developed a 'political ecology framework' in their interactions with each other, as well as with the state, the Non-Governmental Organisations (NGOs) who offer developmental aid, and with academics like Escobar who conduct research in the region.[57] The result is a defense of place which takes into account biodiversity, sustainability, traditional production systems, cultural rights, and ethnic identities – all the while engaging with those transnational networks which assist in promoting and protecting their local way of life.[58]

The idea of place and how to interpret it is, as demonstrated above, constantly moving and expanding; it has attracted many scholars, from a variety of fields. A quick look at the collection of critical essays by

---

55 Arturo Escobar, 'Culture Sits in Places: Reflections on Globalism and Subaltern Strategies of Localization', *Political Geography* 20 (2001): 166.
56 Escobar, p. 141.
57 Escobar, p. 160.
58 Escobar, p. 163.

Hubbard and Kitchin, entitled *Key Thinkers on Space and Place*, reveals a list of more than sixty authors as diverse as Benedict Anderson, Homi Bhabha, Judith Butler, Edward Said, Raymond Williams and Yi-Fu Tuan.[59] The collection attests to the diverse ways in which space and place can be theorized: from humanism to Marxism, feminism to post-structuralism, and queer theory to post-colonialism. The Australian philosopher Jeff Malpas assists in accounting for this diversity of interest and approach:

> It is not surprising that place, and associated notions of spatiality and embodiment, should have come to such prominence in so many different disciplines and in the work of so many different writers and researchers. The ubiquity of place, and the diversity of contexts in which it appears, is. . . some testament to the significance of the notion, but just as the concept of place seems to appear in so many different places, so it seems that the concept is also dispersed and fragmented.[60]

Such multiplicity of method also affects ideas about how culture is considered in the context of expanding horizons and dissolving boundaries. In his discussion

---

59 Phil Hubbard and Rob Kitchin (eds.), *Key Thinkers on Space and Place* (Los Angeles and London: Sage, 2011).
60 J.E. Malpas, *Place and Experience: A Philosophical Topography* (Cambridge: Cambridge UP, 1999), p. 13.

of 'new voices' in Northern Irish poetry and place, Kennedy-Andrews writes:

> The concept of a fixed, unitary and bounded culture founded on notions of place, kinship, parish, nation, religious belief and the continuity of tradition, has had to give way to a sense of fluid and permeable cultural identity, [which] is re-imagined in terms of constant interrelation and mixing of cultural influences. Places are porous, more open, products of links with other places rather than exclusive enclosures marked off from the outside world.[61]

Certain aspects of these developments may be seen in the work contained in this anthology. Many pieces are set in Belfast: a place which has been, according to Edna Longley, difficult to characterise effectively, because it is a complex, multi-layered, multi-classed space with a burgeoning and diverse population.[62] The validity of this assertion is even more apparent now than when Longley was writing in the mid-1990s. The range of places treated in this collection extends far beyond Northern Ireland to include the United States, the Caribbean,

---

61 *Writing Home*, p. 284. Among the 'new voices' in Northern Irish poetry who interrogate received identities and concepts of home Kennedy-Andrews considers Peter McDonald, Sinead Morrissey, Alan Gillis, and Leontia Flynn.

62 Edna Longley, '"A Barbarous Nook": The Writer and Belfast', in *The Living Stream: Literature and Revisionism in Ireland.* (Newcastle-up-on-Tyne: Bloodaxe Books, 1994), pp. 86-108.

South Africa, the European continent, and even (albeit tangentially) outer space. We may search in vain for an all-encompassing definition of place which will suit everyone's needs; but the fact that the writing has moved from the local towards the global is in itself significant.

As this is a literary analysis, perhaps the best that can be offered as an insight into the significance of place is an appeal to language. In the 1990s Tuan observed:

> Language is important to students of place not only because Thomas Hardy or Willa Cather has written evocatively on landscape, and has thus provided a literary standard that geographers should seek to emulate in their own writing; rather language is important – indeed central – because humans are language animals, and language is a force that all of us use everyday to build, sustain, and destroy. . . . Taking language seriously shows. . . that the "quality" of place is more than just aesthetic or affectional, that it also has a *moral* dimension.[63]

These words imply that effective assessments of place need to display an awareness of rights, duties, responsibilities, and purpose. If the writings in this volume are seen in that context, then they will serve as useful contributions to this endlessly fascinating, continually evolving debate.

---

63 Yi-Fu Tuan, 'Language and the Making of Place: A Narrative-Descriptive Approach', *Annals of the Association of American Geographers* 81.4 (1991): 694; emphasis original.

POETRY

THE LIGHTS
Alan Gillis

Green is for go and red for going no-
where as my brother drums his fingers in
a rhythm on my head. Sister says
the lights and he takes up the wheel,
turning left and driving through a rainbow
coalition of well-heeled mannequins
in hyper-lit titillated go-go displays,
burnt homes under boarding and real
deal posters frayed upon bookies and bars,
in which I'd embark upon a fifteen-year binge
to block out the hard eyes, this advice in the car
filled with sun, a honey-centred lozenge:
buck yourself up, don't you know you are …
He breaks off, uncertain. The lights are orange.

WHO IS YOUR CITY?
Medbh McGuckian

The canal's middle swells with waiting
For odd hours of night in the middle of the day.
North appears everywhere, the now of the snow,
Warming ice counts itself away in different
Sun angles, like a block of frozen ink
Insisting on the line. The water knows
The way down, to the Titanic and her two
Sisters. She rouges her silver likeness,
Buttons her gown herself, so high, so closed,
Her days malodorous from saturated skies.

Do you think it reflects well on our city
To ones who arrived only a week ago
To go outdoors in pyjamas to the turgid
Bar district, the Gucci outlets in the city's
Revamped living room? To photograph
A child on the King's highway?
Arrival city – where disaster zones have become
More theatrical, ambitious parks obsessed
With self-esteem are honey-combed
With missions and endeavours and offers
Of salvation as an incandescent life-force.

Gone is the edginess of the city, cleansed
Of conflict, argument, debate, protest, ructions
And ribaldry, notwithstanding the spy cameras,
The pop-up-shops, the flash mobs of drink-
Fuelled petrolheads, the new Purple Flag award.
I still have to define my life through the false prism
Of Samson and Goliath, the ailing road perfuming
The heavy curtains of Parliament. We still show
Our papers to reveal where we are going.

The street will no longer lie like a doormat
But plunge stories down on to swift pavements
Pedal-powered by driverless taxis. Nobody's
Living there, nobody's moved in, it's sitting there
Though the visitor centre is shut and they are
Lifting the paddy fields on to the roof
Which smells too much of museum dust or pages
From faded magazines. The waterfront within
The enabling bygone hedges is made of flesh.
I speak the language, I know how to be a woman here.

ST. ANNE'S
Laura Cameron

I telephoned earlier,
asked them to turn the book
to the right page.

A grandfather clock stands,
time frozen,
near the front of the cathedral;

eleven minutes past twelve.
I search for signs of life.
The Book of Remembrance

is encased in oak.
Her name, in black ink,
has five strangers for company.

My finger traces
calligraphed letters
through cold glass.

Further on, a flower-shaped
window – a man clothed in crimson
on blue background, arms raised.

Giving thanks or praying
for deliverance? Closer now,
I read the caption –

Jonah spent three days
in the belly of a whale.
I smooth my hair,

drop two pound coins
in the donations barrel,
retrieve my rickety umbrella.

I descend six stone steps;
hear my other daughter's voice
counting.

COMMERCIAL COURT
John D. Kelly

A pair of fit racing pigeons
    decide to break off from the flock
on their way home, and are making
      out on a parapet, with the ferals

above *Commercial Court*;
        above rows
of hanging light bulbs
      spanning between red
brick walls
    rising out of wet cobbles.

On one is a red heart —
    an old Guinness sign fixed over
a red bench with a brass plaque,
      beside a red fire bucket
filled with sand (and butts),
     on double yellow lines.

Above crows, in a clearing sky,
    is a peregrine surveying them;
eerily 'eagle-eyed' from afar

        waiting
for that murder to pass
        waiting

for her to have had enough

                                                  waiting

for her to rise up, with him

            (in a clap flap) flying after her

totally distracted — oblivious

to the sound of his own starter pistol.

IN A GLASS HOUSE
(Tropical Ravine, Botanic Gardens, Belfast)
Gráinne Tobin

This gangway
   where your footsteps sound
is your panopticon
   you must keep vigil

glass furred and fogged
   in steam-bath dankness
all beyond
   blotted and blurred

sweetheart ferns
   spread and cling
to soaking brickwork
   mossy sills

the drip the tap
   the run of moisture
liquid percussion
   creaking branches

released from bedsits
   parlour palms
and castor oil plants
   swell to giants

in hanging baskets
  succulent antlers
trail from insect-
  fretted sconces

drowsing festoons
  of pitcher-plants
penis gourds
  Aladdin's lamps

do not pinch out
  the withered shoots
 or steal camellias
  for slip or blossom

try not to cross
  the species barrier
rubbing your cheek
  on leaves of striped velvet

you may be tempted
  to court oblivion
under white blooms
  of angels' trumpets

no throwing coins
  into the pond
in the garden
  of life and death

CONFLICT TOURISM
(Belfast, NI)
Erika Meitner

People here think my accent
is charming because America
is young. Today at the Friday bakery
filled with old ladies I asked about
raisin buns piled in the glass case,
and the woman behind the counter
volunteered that she had family
in Philadelphia. I don't understand
the kinds of bread here—there are
so many. Bread always feels elemental,
and moving is a time-honored way
to improve one's condition. Bap. Farl.
Wheaten. Soda. Barmbrack. People migrate.
I have moved here, as long as they're willing
to maintain me, but I am an empty Beaux-Arts
palace. Here, all of the restaurants place
long white taper candles on every table.
Even for breakfast, they are lit.
In silver holders. In candelabras.
Here, the streets are always wet,
though I never see it rain. The darkness
is pervasive. At home there is snow.
At home the bones of a dog rest
on a fire escape, and everywhere sirens

have a long history of catastrophe. It is
our job to see only the person in front of us—
not the stereotype—but I am American,
and many here feel America should be
taken apart with a screwdriver. Maybe
it already has been. I've been gone that long.
I no longer wear my youth like buzzing electrons.
A map is permission to get lost, but here
the neighborhoods are well-marked
by their inhabitants: people who don't
take no for an answer. It isn't safe there.
It isn't safe here. The graffiti says I'll put
a bullet in your head. Says fuck the world. But
I have to wake up at a reasonable hour
to take my son to swim lessons.
Most art grows out of normality.
How do they identify the enemy here
when everyone looks the same? Names.
Accents. Boundary lines. We preserve
the past by taming it so there are stories,
and always more stories.

DISCONNECTED
Lindsay Hodges

The bed they had delivered in emergency –
too short by one foot seven inches,
that cramps his limbs, his ankles,
leaves scratches as he tries to stretch
against the backboard,
the one I phone about to social workers
and the care team and the district nurses
and the hospice tumour specialist
every half hour,
the one in which he dreams that Steve McQueen
will rescue him from Alcatraz –
is sitting in our living room,
legs slotting into grooves already gouged
into the carpet seven years ago.

I listen to the mattress as it exhales, refills,
gasps at intervals in tandem with the monitors,
the strangled catheter, puff of fresh air dispenser –
a brand I'll never use again –
sharp intake of blood pressure cuff
as duty nurses work the shifts, unravel him.

He wants to die here, like my mother,
facing outwards towards the window that he wants
uncurtained,
watching cherry blossom blizzards,
pieris raining flame onto azalea,
at night the pipistrelles that skim for midges,
wheeking up and down the conifers,
where moon is filtering through the violet cloud
onto the landscape painting
we bought for him on his retirement,
its light a prism on the cabinet-imprisoned
cut-glass flutes I have not dusted for 3 months.

When the time comes,
when this bed is disconnected,
we will all be gone.
This is not home.

DRAWING BY VISITOR
Erika Meitner

the gates to the gardens shut at four o'clock
the second misconception about the conflict
dark comes early
its roots go back
I hear his accent everywhere
what they had witnessed
on the street on the way to the bank
what they had suffered
on the street on the way to the market to get milk
there are always exceptions
on the street where the bouncers raise themselves up
    in doorways
there are always incompatible ends
on the street the light is slick orange, sickly yellow
a strategy that inflicted great damage
it is late and the cars keep rushing
the decommissioned arsenals
dark expands to fill the streets
the foreseeable future
our first night, we went out on a walk
the restoration of devolution
it had been so long since we'd lived in a city of any
    kind
the shopkeepers in their blue jackets
we raised our arms from our sides to be searched

the shopkeepers in their grey coats
I remember his laundry on the line
the shopkeepers in their red kerchiefs bent at the waist
I remember my shoes and my coat
sweeping up broken glass

SUNDAYS AT ST. AGNES'
Pauline Brady

We love our Sundays,
Heading out to St. Aggie's disco,
Appropriately dressed for Da's inspection.
The real disco gear hidden in the mate's house
(Her da doesn't care about her).
Hastily changing into the latest trend: Minis, Midis,
   Maxis
And Hotpants – What were they like?
Slap on the faces, glitter on the cheeks,
High heels clacking
And we're off!

Sunday 30th January 1972.
We're off as usual;
Me and the girls.
   Click-clacking our way down Slievegallion Hill
In our latest platforms.
I'm feeling tall – Five feet five tonight
Four eleven and a half in my stocking feet.
We're waffling about who fancies who,
Who's a great lumber?
Who kisses like a vacuum cleaner?
Who's going to touch?
Who's the DJ?
The usual teenage preoccupations.
T. Rex concerns us more than Civil Rights marches.

Our glittered faces gleaming,
Our moves previously polished to perfection in
    bedrooms,
We dance to 'Ride a White Swan'.
We're incensed as the DJ stops us mid-boogie to make
    an announcement:
    'Two people shot dead in Derry'.
We don't have time to let the news sink in as the
    updates begin –
'No there's four. No eight—'
And on and on and on.
No more dancing, no more eyeing up the local talent.
The stunned silence is palpable.
The murmuring and muttering begins and then the
    raging roaring.

And we're off – out the doors.
We stampede past the ashen-faced priest
Who's been hastily summoned in a vain bid to restore
    order.
No chance!
We're moving as one – no leaders making plans
(That will come later),
Just a raging, roaring torrent of teenage wrath.
Onto the Andytown Road
Moves the smouldering sea of venom.
Flagstones are ripped from the ground.
Armed with bottles, bricks and stones

The riot ensues.
It will be the first of many.

Later, as I stand in the rubble,
The glitter on my face smeared and smudged and
    smoke-ridden,
I view the aftermath –
The Co-op's in flames, (no more Co-quarters for our
    mas),
Grimley's, Collins's, and the rest.
Squat in the debris, broken-windowed and battered,
Their paint and powder mingling on the ruptured
    flags.
Only St. Agnes' chapel remains sedate and untouched,
Surveying the damage.
Thirteen dead, as many maimed, one who will die
    later.
Among them seven teenage boys who will never get to
    boogie to Bolan again.
And I know our Sundays will never be the same.
The word 'Para' has become a venomous spit on teenage
    Irish tongues.
The faint but terrible odour of irrevocable change
    hovers in the fume-filled air,
As we drag our broken heels back up the hill to face
    the parents.

TURN AGAIN
Ciaran Carson

There is a map of the city which shows the bridge that
　　was never built.
A map which shows the bridge that collapsed; the
　　streets that never existed.
Ireland's Entry, Elbow Lane, Weigh-House Lane, Back
　　lane, Stone-Cutter's Entry—
Today's plan is already yesterday's — the streets that
　　were there are gone.
And the shape of the jails cannot be shown for
　　security reasons.

The linen backing is falling apart — the Falls Road
　　hangs by a thread.
When someone asks me where I live, I remember
　　where I used to live.
Someone asks me for directions, and I think again. I
　　turn into
A side-street try to throw off my shadow, and history
　　is changed.

PRIDE
Laura Cameron

I stand firm on Royal Avenue
to witness the parade.
Meanwhile, at the City Hall gates,
two women
in Union Jack wellies
kick against the erosion
of their cultural identity.

Infectious music,
thousands of spectators
smiling,
swaying to the beat;
two grannies in the front row
jiggle toddlers in buggies.
I let rainbow waves
wash over me.

I can't believe we've got here!
Belfast, twenty-thirteen.
My mind wanders...
In years to come
when school peers ask,
'Are your parents a mixed marriage?'
will a child respond,
'Yeah. My Da's a man
and my Ma's a woman'?

DUNLUCE AVENUE
Moyra Donaldson

At each evening's return
you hold the key ready,
push the light switch in
and race the timer two flights
to your bedsit before the hall
and stairs are taken over again
by darkness. This is a house
of dingy melancholy, you're
spooked by it, wish you'd
never moved here, you're
lonely here; it's all wrong.

Be reassured, thirty years from now,
you will have forgotten most things
about this place; no memory
remaining of furniture, décor,
the particular fear

but you will remember
the professor of Japanese,
elderly and rumpled, soft
as a feather pillow and sad
as a lost empire: his footsteps
across the floor above
in the long hours before dawn.

How you used to wait
for the knock on your door.
Open it, he will be there
holding a jar of warm sake.

SUNSET ON THE FOYLE
Lindsay Hodges

I have come to love this river
in my passing through,
hear its cadence from a distance,
could find my way there blindfold,
siren-called,
know it best in the half-light of the morning walk
when it seems like it's not moving,
as if its heartrate slows down overnight,
needs first bird to start it beating –
touch of Herons and of Teal,
of passing wings of Buzzards to the playing fields.

In afternoons I'm over it –
across the bridge that blows your socks off,
looking down at just how vast it is,
how it separates the city,
great tracts of mudflats visible on either side,
the woods where brambles cloak the Scarlet Elf Caps,
where rushes hide the Kingfisher,
until that blue flame flash of his lit touchpaper.

I never thought to witness sun set fire to water –
but when we see it start to happen,
you fly the car down from the heights
to reach a vantage point
just in the instant that the last light
grapples with the dusk,
clouds stained grey and pink and golden,
and here I find my place, belong.

HOPE
Deirdre Devine

A bridge rises
over a river
that flows and flows
and does not hear
what went before
or fears what is to come:

a gift for our present,
a step from our past,
a beacon in white
to catch the light of our future,
a walk of peace for our children,
a rainbow over the Foyle.

GHOST EDEN
(– after Anthony Haughey's 'Settlement')
Erika Meitner

Garden of rock.
Garden of brick and heather.
        Garden of cranes with their hands raised
as if they know the yellow answer:
        to gather together—safety in numbers.
Garden of drywall frames, holes for windows
        punched out like teeth. Garden of bar fights.
Garden of rubble and gaps,
        spectral for-sale signs knocked
from wooden posts, bleached down
        to numbers ending in gardens of overgrown lots.
We are falling into ruin, garden
        of scaffolding and shale and gravel—
give us back our peace: a half-built garden
        of theft, treasures hidden in darkness,
newspapers crumpled on subfloors telling us
        to hold fast to that which is good.
Garden of rebar and saplings with trunks
        encased in corrugated piping
because many animals can girdle
        a tree's bark quickly: deer, stray cats, rabbits.
Garden of Tyvek wrap loosed
        and flapping like a ship's sail

in the gales, in the sheeting storms.

    Hanging laundry left out in the garden
past darkness, fruit from the tree

    of human-ness: socks, shirts, underpants.
Garden of long exposures, half-light, traces

    that empty themselves in tire treads running
like ladders through red clay mud:

    the dirt from which we are formed
and crushed and formed again.

NO SURE ACRE
James A Simpson

What if the North blasts snatch dry at the stone walls,
stripping the lichen,
bleaching bare the ribs of the man
with no sure acre?

What if hunger scourges his skin
and leeches his land
when there's no gentle inglenook
to hide him when the spectres come,
no hook on which to hang his workaday clothes
in the gloaming?

Where does he go for comfort then in the long pitch
    black,
when his chair screeches sharp
on the quarry tiles
and dust singes acrid on the grey coiled elements
of his electric bar heater,
when he yanks the worn knob of his larder door
to find a single egg
and a tin of Del Monte peaches, two years out of date,
when his calendar yellows and the pulse of the
    Woolworth's clock rattles off beat,
and time drags ninety minutes slow?

How will he stanch the wind sucking at him through
    slaps,
making free with his space,
sweeping over his chipped linoleum?

What forces made him settle for the hunched up
    crackle of
The Belfast News Letter,
The Irish News,
the fizz of a distant radio station,
the solitary slip slide of King James' silken pages,
night after night
or prayers to St Jude?

Whom does he turn to as he quenches the hard glare
    of a hundred naked watts,
slamming a defensive bolt home,
alone at ten, eleven or twelve,
scaling the cracked stairs in stocking feet
to the sheetless cot he shares with shadows?

Tomorrow he will prise more small potatoes from the
    earth,
hoking them into the future from the tight patch
    behind the byre,
furtive as ever in the early half light,
alert as a blackbird.

But for now
He settles his bentness into the curvature of the
    horsehair
where, lost in its depth
his hacked fingers patrol the ticking,
probing the mattress,
searching,
stretching for his loaded revolver
before he tries for sleep,
untouched by the Sacred Heart
or
the embroidered scripture verse above his head,
telling him he is worth more than many sparrows.

HARBOUR
Paul Maddern

Groomsport's tenders settle to their weightier sides.
Plastic oil-carton buoys float inches above slack rope
　　cables.
The derelict trawler, 'Red Shamrock', finally gets the
　　joke
and beneath its prow a man in oilskins digs for bait
remembering when harbours drew sons to their fathers.
As the last emphasis of evening pinks the Copeland
　　Islands
and the lighthouse stutters,
retired couples in cars fold the final edition
and head home for convenience store teas.

A seal comes up for air in the bay.
Three kids skipping stones arrest their arms mid throw
and follow its progress with cartoon stealth tactics,
betting on where it's likely to surface.
They descend the ladder at the end of the pier
and in the spill of a Gatsby-green landing light,
like sailors in rigging, hold on with one hand and lean
　　out,
loyal until the seal is at large in the Irish Sea.
The lighthouse flares. The Copelands opal.

ON VISITING THE ISLAND OF MY ANCESTORS (Copeland Island, County Down)
Stephanie Conn

A hand gripped, then pulled, to lift my body
from the boat. My foot finds the moving metal
grille, slips on sea-green fibres. I watch my step.

The land is cushion-soft and punctured by rabbit holes.
The field by the shore sprouts patches of rigid grass
and bluebells. On the hill there is a scattering

of broken shell and bone. The skull of a small bird,
stripped bare, reveals teeth at the end of the beak,
eye-socket shaped spaces. The brain's imprint remains.

A single step is enough the send a flock of black-
capped Eider duck to the sky, their green napes
flashing. Their cries are long and hoarse.

I taste salt at the back of my throat, raise cold hands
to my ears to drown out the screech the gulls
are making, keep clear of the south-facing cliffs;

the dive and swoop and squawk of them draws me in.
Exposed nests litter the rocks, soften the lichen-covered
ridges, hold blue-grey speckled eggs, in threes.

Five steps back, and silent, I watch one crack –
see shadows shift behind the splitting case, before
a tiny beak emerges – opens and closes, opens again.

GREBA CRAS*
Moyra Donaldson

We have disturbed the crows
into a fierce wing-clattering
croaking black circling,
threatening to wake the dead,
but the dead stay sleeping,

all *God's lovely loans*
crowded together, tumbled
together: nothing to distinguish
one bone from another now.

Depending on the soil, type
of wood, it's about a year,
two at most, until a coffin
collapses in on itself.

Four hundred years of headstones
and over the wall, older stories still,
the Manx princess, her abbey
of thanksgiving for safe landing,

the monks, wrapping their cloaks
around themselves, becoming crows;
out above all walls, flying into the arms
of the village women, who waited
in their beds for the sound of wings.

* Ulster Scots for 'Greyabbey Crows'

THE ENGINE ROOM
Norman Meharry

Seems like it can't be all in there,
Below the plate deck and superstructure
So much space between the sweating bulkheads.
Levels below levels, adjunct to
The sweat-beast of the Doxford engine
That is tethered within our ship,
The guts of thrusting horse-power
Expressed down a shaft to the screw
That churns the water by the stern.

I'd no right to be there, peeking down
From the main into the oily light,
Berated by the oven-air, the diesel-breath
Leeched of oxygen. The smack of noise
That no speech, shout, yell, or scream could rise above,
Ensuring insanity.
I'd spy the few troglodytes in boilers,
Acolytes to the stagger dance of
Eight giant pistons punching up
Into the height above,
Attending the beast by
Oiling this and greasing that.

These same attendants would return from there
To here in the superstructure,
Showered and in civvies,
To the mess to eat and drink
And smoke with the rest of us,
And throw darts.
A dazed young sixer tottered in one watch
To where I kept the bar.
Deathly pale and blubbering,
Still in his boiler,
'My Mother,' he blurted as a sob,
'I've heard her speak to me,
Down there in that awful fucking place.'
'How, in all that noise?' we asked.
'I heard her most clear.'
A rough-hewn Geordie he was.
He wiped his snot on his wrist,
And muffled his tears.

MISSED
Annemarie Mullan

Her noisy absence lingers
in the tiny things –

a lipstick stain upon
the cushion of a rattan chair,

the hair-dyed towel we use
to wipe the bathroom floor

the odd mascara cotton bud
fished from the laundry pile.

Her crimplene dresses, pencil cases
toys and bits and bobs,

are in a box. It's just a matter of time
before these go to War On Want.

She's the relatives' favourite topic
when she's missed from family snaps,

and although her quarterly appointments
and voting slips still come,

the strains of all-night radio have stopped
since her younger brother got her room.

Our telephone is tingling from last night's call –
says when she's more settled

she'll send a big long newsy letter
and cuttings from all her potted succulents.

ABSENCE
Teresa Kane

I

A long bog walk as ragged light faded
from a late summer sky.
Hand in hand we leaned into silence.
The curlew haunted its cry
and the skylark brought us to fix on absence.

Between turf bank and rowan ditch
we found it: an ancient wishing well.
Leaning over to drop pennies
into old waters we dreamed
beyond our knowing.

II

Today in the back yard you waited for me.
I knew it was you by your smile,
your hands squeezed into pockets.

We were near yet I didn't
taste your breath on my lips.
Were you breathing?

Today in the back yard I knew you were sorry
because a butterfly brushed my cheek
and distant clouds rumbled in a far-away sky.

I knew you were gone when wood
pigeons fell silent and wind shushed
through forest trees.

I knew you were gone when gathered rain
cried on my upturned face, glistening on foxgloves...
pooling on the empty garden seat.

III

I am not going to speak about hawthorn trees
that hedge around old fields or hares that
run with the moon.

I am not going to speak again
of skylark or curlew,
foxgloves, bluebells or summer days

that spill out sunshine.
You are gone and I can no longer hold you,
stretch my arms around your waist

or slip into your jacket,
your hand, your thoughts.
Sometimes I dream you back

and hold you there;
as nettle holds raindrop
just before it falls.

WINDOWS
Mia Mouron-Adams

One barred
One not
One latch
One lock

One sunset
One sunrise
Two eyes:
Two eyes

One view.

THE BARN
Therese Kieran

On March 17th in her eightieth year we walked the
    road to Quinns',
cut through Mary's immaculate yard, let the mad dogs
    at Meegans' lie.
We photographed the humble barn so she might arc
    her brush,
stroke canvas with tints and tones, grey corrugations
    against the sky.
A smile the wrong way round, lunula topping solid
    stone,
its flesh and bone stood eighty years or more, bowed
    towards the chapel.

I pictured its red doors flung wide, drawing in the
    meal and hay,
staples of winter feeding, or slight slip through the
    wicket door,
unbeknownst to kith or kin, giving and sharing
    secrets;
the barn made no confession, they could take all that
    next door.
We took the narrow passage down the yard, met Mary
    with her barrow,
as unconcerned as if she saw us every day, on this spot
    passing through.

My mother photographed the dog, a spaniel: a hunter
    with no bark,
tethered but safe from a road full of 'Harry the hares'.
His sentry cousin yards away, patrols as if to wake the
    dead.
And up past the Bog Road, two spinning collies pivot
    in mid air;
twirling feather dusters; pirouettes of black and white,
adding howl and yelp beneath the wou wou flapping
    of wild geese.

We look up, wait for the splash, the gentle ripple
    riding a breeze
as they land on the green ridge lake below; and I am
    taken by her smile,
the sheer delight and pleasure of drinking it in;
    country sights and sounds,
the comfort of familiar and her joy in nature's endless
    bounty.
I am left to imagine a painting that declares her
    attachment to Glassdrummond;
a rich narrative of how one has settled, how one has
    communed with the other.

LINES AT LACKEN MILL
Paul Maddern

> *How lovely it is today!*
> *The sunlight breaks and flickers*
> *On the margin of my book.*
>   –9th Century Irish marginalia

The shower has passed but rain
drops from the canopy to play the river like a drum
and I'm absorbed by the performance
of a wayward beat falling on the page.
The *a* in apple blossoms and the *b*
in beauty blooms, infecting with the bleed
all well-meaning words.

                  And just as well.

For I would tell you simply
that the mill cat rests beside me, the dog
transfixed by swans. I would write
of an ancient weir broking for a race;
of herds pastured for millennia
lapping waters that a heron scours;
of the Erne's remorseless measure
over worn, familial rocks
and of eddies they maintain for dedicated salmon.
I would even reach and reference linnet's wings
but you have heard all this and are immune.

Perhaps a fashion's passed
as these spots in time diminish.
Still, I'll take some pleasure
from the seamless finish:
a single note magnificat,
climax to the great tympanic act,
falls then fades in the quickening river.

And now the page is parched. Old *a*'s and *b*'s
that advocated venture have been stemmed.
But you, attuned to perfect labours, prove
dried blooms and blossoms will be shamed
when, shortly, we will witness birth again.

MOVILLA CEMETERY
Moyra Donaldson

It's beautiful here, high as Scrabo's crag and tail,
looking down on the lough of many harbours
and across to the Mournes, landscape singing
through the bones; chromatic scale of home.

Easter, Christmas, anniversaries, the living come,
each to their own: *beloved husband; dearest daughter;*
each *sadly missed.* They bring flowers and dampened
cloths to wipe the gravestones clear of droppings, moss.

Remembering and forgetting, memory and dust.
Century upon century of story: Ulster kings; Finian
and the word of Christ; the war hero; the provost;
my mother, who thought it was a cold place, always

wanted to be returned to an earlier belonging.
She's contented here at last, accepting of the earth
and my father lying beside her, for it's my story
now; for a time I am the word and the telling of home.

I will be buried here, in the grave my husband bought.
Belonging sings to me here, and I am singing back.

THRUPENNY MOON
Teresa Kane

You turned up like bits of broken clay pipes
found buried in river mud by Dane's Mill.

With your hare lip and flattened fringe
you mumbled about sheltering ditches,

clamped turf, neighbours and fierce rain.
You shadowed out-houses, haysheds, crab apple

trees and the road that distanced onto Harte's Height.
And I still young enough to be strange

waded behind in the sheugh and sluice
of your words.

CROSSROADS
Martelle Mc Partland

My blind grandmother
Danced in the small space
Between the hearth
And the chair
Remembering the Madden Road
And the lantern in the hollow
Of the tree at the
Crossroads.

In that small space
Between the hearth
And the chair she
Danced remembering
How the villagers
Gathered to watch
Her on a Saturday
Night at the Crossroads.

With the applause of
The dead in her head
The no warning
Bomb exploded
And in the rubble
Between the chair and the
Hearth my blind grandmother
Danced again at the
Crossroads.

BEHIND THE NET CURTAIN
Laura Cameron

Mrs Johnson,
pink-lipped, white-toothed,
tells me to go on up.

Boy George the cat
worries a bluebottle trapped
behind the net curtain.

I find her barefoot,
stone-washed Lee jeans,
oversized checked shirt.

I offer my present.
She lifts her shirt to show me,
still can't button her jeans –

belly tanned from Majorca,
a fifteenth birthday treat.
Just a fortnight ago

she cried down the phone,
told me about the blue line.
Her parents sorted everything.

Mrs Johnson appears,
two glasses of Coke and
six Jammie Dodgers

on a flowery tray.
She reverses out, Boy George
weaving through her legs.

The uniform hangs limp
on her wardrobe door.
She'll be back on Monday,

back to normal, she says.
Heading for the front door
my nose tingles with fresh paint.

Mr Johnson asks what I think
of the Sunshine Yellow. Lovely, I say.
I preferred the old Midnight Blue.

AT THE GATE
Kathryn Baird

They've kept the Hound Lemon paint,
echo of the young brave,
hero of the Uladh,
who gave his name
to their home, Cullo Hill.

I think he lived in the rath,
that ancient stronghold
down the lane
protected by banks of earth,
a round enclosure
where our sons took wing
on swings and trampoline,
and buried pets
beneath a fretwork of oak.

Our fence of tumbling gorse
has been replaced
by rows of solar lights,
black metal gates with spikes,
handles like padlocks.
Yet the bush I planted,
exochorda macrantha – the bride –
extends its tendrils,
reaching out to me.

From where I stand I cannot know
if my mother's caragana tree
still blooms, or if the door's still blue,
bright as the days
when each of our three boys
stood beneath the fanlight
posing for photos
on their first day at school,
their shoulders weighted down
by brand new satchels,
their P1 ties askew.

Inside the house is mystery now,
though the view of the mountains
must be the same:
a shadowed presence glimpsed through trees,
down sweeping lawns, across parterres,
from tall windows where one Christmas
we watched the snowflakes fall
and thought of Joyce's
'The Dead'.

THE ERNE RUSHES THROUGH ME
Moyra Donaldson

A great clean flood to rinse away
the whole of the tired, wicked world.

A heron guards the dreaming ivory gates,
my eyes have turned the blue of damselfly;
red gilled perch and silver trout,
swim through the ventricles of my heart
and swallows rise from my throat, stitching
my thoughts to the sky: it is as if nothing

bad is happening anywhere: as if
everything in the Garden is lovely.

WHITE ROCKS BEACH
Siobhan Scullion

Six seagulls sail above us and you are still,
except for the movement of your breath carried
along by the wind and mingled with salt and foam.

Nature has laid out for us a blanket of pebble
and stone; alabaster white, dove grey and slate blue
are laced together, a composition of colour.

I try to make conversation, fill our silence with childish
talk as though the sea sharing its stories with you,
the waves whispering in your ear, is not enough.

You are not concerned with surfers soaring across
the waves, you are not so bothered about ice cream
on the way home.

While I foolishly try to steer your course, you are
present only in this moment and this place. For the
briefest of moments you anchor me to the shore.

Captivated by the waves, you fix your eyes ahead
and I see your little life stretch long beyond me,
far out into the sea.

THE PLANTER'S DAUGHTER
Julie Agnew

These are not her roots. They were firmed in other
    soil and fostered here;
twining, infusing, till old knows not and new fears not
and home is peace in a land of giants, bound tight by sea.
Where the air crackles with more than possibility
and voices low and fast speak words with magic in
    their soul
hewn from the same rock she is planted on.
No approval sought by this daughter of the Plantation
clutching at the dreams of others, to knit with her own
in a language she does not understand.
Here the native son will seek the Planter's Daughter
with her new soul and voice unlike his own,
feet dipped in the waves, Medusa's coils around her head,
where the rush and soothe has scoured her prints,
where she waits to dance.

ANKLE SOCKS IN JUNE
Teresa Kane

In summer she sat
outside Campbell's shop
Feet splayed to balance
her unsteady world

She shredded newspaper
into a basket
grey sentences heaped
in sensless bundles;

a confetti of chaos
like the words she shouted
to neighbours and strangers
as they stopped to talk to her
about clear skies with no rain.

I thought it strange
that a grown woman
should wear ankle socks
identical to mine.

TAKING THE BOAT
Annemarie Mullan

When she was grown up (she'd often thought)
she'd take the boat like all those country girls
in Edna's books, who wore smart frocks
and drank fine wine with handsome men
who'd buy them flowers and dazzle them
with foreign food while they'd converse.

The first she heard when she emerged
from the distance of a general anaesthetic
were the accents of the Pakistani doctor
and the English orderly, holding a radio
out the window to get the best reception
for some international cricket match.

The Irish girls in the other metal beds
all cowed and shy, were murmuring
in soft low sleepy tones. Some moaned.
One, bolder than the rest, declared
that she had just popped out from work;
had told her boss that she was with a client.

She gave the other ones, who asked, precise
directions to a friendly hostel and the dole.
Not one was going back. They said that they
would never want to face the rest at home
who'd know or guess why they had upped
and gone away to England in the first place.

BERLIN*
Matthew McKay

The best representation of its country.
Tall skyscrapers that pierce the heavens like bumps in
    God's floor.
People constantly moving. Never stopping.
Their choir of chatter, the hypnotic march of their
    footsteps, the percussion of trains and the fanfare of
    car horns are the parade of its progress.
The smells of its foods are omnipresent, wafting
    through the air, haunting the streets with their
    lingering scent.
Its roads are its blood and its people the cells.
    Supplying oxygen. Supplying life.

*Inspired by a postcard of the city of Berlin.

BEACH PEBBLE
Mario Abbatiello

I comb the places where poems lurk.
Sometimes I try
to capture and tame them, but often
I let them be, preferring them wild
like the one living in the purple shadow
of the white-streaked grey pebble
that speaks to me of healing, recalls
the day it found me on the beach at
Deception Pass, and travelled with me
across a continent and an ocean to my desk
where it has sat whispering this last decade.

NON-LIEUX
Erika Meitner

Hand-painted on the side
of a shack we pass
on the road to Ohio:
what this world comin to

This is not haiku. This
is more like fog and we're
socked in and your body

is invisible and right
across from me
simultaneously.

How much ammo you got?
says one guy to another
in the cola-chip aisle
of the Food Lion.

The fortitude of rain
hitting the roof:
percussive sadness.

Almost-saved is not
good enough, says
the church sign. We were
out of ketchup again.

Did you see what he
put on Pete's grave and
what he put on Junior's?

says the woman in
the Bob Evans bath-
room stall with a cane.

It was sprained, not
broken. From high up,
from far away.

He was still working
at that bar in town,
after all these years,

assigned to a circum-
scribed position, like
the supermoon, like
employee parking.

In the dark 7-11 lot
two officers approach
a white van, flashlights on
and held overhand.

The church sign says
living without God
is like dribbling a football.

The light, it was too bright
to be captured in
an iPhone photo

where people are not
the urgency of the
present moment.

*Did you get it squared
away?* asks one man to
another at the Starbucks
condiment counter.

One of the officers
has a hand on his
holster. What is he
saying to the driver?

The church sign touts
tonight's sermon: Entering
the Miraculous Zone.

There were no grounds
for prosecution. I left
before I heard
the answer.

EMERALD ISLE, NORTH CAROLINA
Therese Kieran

In a pink dress, with a pink pen,
I write of North Carolina.
On an Emerald Isle unlike my own,
warm breezes tease and tickle
toes in shady recline.

Scratching heels in hot sand,
I marvel at unruly waves
stretching miles from home;
arriving tepid on a sleepy shore.

Giddy with excitement – a week to taste
this ocean view and savour it a lifetime.
Day breaks with deafening crashes,
Night falls with soporific splash and wash,

And oh the night of the Super Moon,
A bright, bouncing balloon blown out of black,
slowly floating up and up,
weaving through webbed cloud
to settle, to glow like lava.

ON HONEY POT ROAD
Christine Leckey

Where the blacktop ran out and dirt took over,
like iron in winter, impassable come the thaw,
but by June smooth and hard as concrete.
To Fred and Mildred's white house, red barn,
ice house, smoke house and chicken coop,
like all the other farms around those parts.
Corn, beans and squash planted in small
neat fields, contained by dry stone and split rail.

Where old Munn's Brook ran through,
lost in its meanderings
forgot its course and made a lazy lake,
where we'd swim with our cousins
on heavy summer afternoons, big guys
swinging out from overhanging branches
to splashes and shouts. Screams to get out,
make way for a water snake, watch it squiggle
across the surface on the hunt for frogs and small fry.

Where my Mother helped Aunt Mildred bake
a week's worth of pies, set them out on the porch to cool.
Treats for the hired men. Men with bent backs,
dungarees and battered felt hats, skin stained
with sun and soil no amount of lye soap
and hot water slopped from the blackened kettle
could ever make clean.

Where Uncle Fred, not one for company,
ignored my Father. Confined himself,
despite the heat, behind closed doors in the barn.

Where we suddenly stopped visiting
when Mildred moved to a rental in town,
cousin Alan joined the Army, Ronnie the Marines.

Where years later, I took my Mother for a drive
to see what remained and she told me,
after that last summer visit, Fred was found
hanging from the tie beam in the barn.

PSYCHOPOMP ON VENICE BEACH
Clodagh Brennan Harvey

For decades now
I've returned again
and again,
hurtled by the waves
against this shore.
I've fought the foam,
kicked the sand,
felt the sand crabs
fleeing my fingers,
pocketed some future memento –
a small shell,
or piece of glass.
I've pondered
or weighed;
fretted
or cried;
strolled with
the half-loved
or wanting to love wholly –
winnings and losings
all etched here,
gone.

You are the continuity
in all this,
the psychopomp
of Venice's dizzying human tableau,
your image familiar to the world
yet arcane, inexplicable.
You skate by
as you always have,
toweringly turbaned,
amplified guitar booming out
anything from Jimi Hendrix
to Gilbert and Sullivan.
I speak to you,
disarmed by
your guilelessness,
the healthy freshness of you,
your perfect teeth.
I buy your CD
as you skate away, ferryman –
proof of our pact.

POSTAMBLE
Paul Maddern

On Sunday walks beneath pink oleander
I'd let loose a week of stored up chat.
You'd select a stick from fallen branches
littering our path to Grape Bay Beach,
strip the remnant twigs and snap it
to the perfect height for your colonial stride,
for the rhythmic flicking out before
then regimental poke into adopted soil.

> The war-filled man on Newlyn's pier
> had chucked the mackerel for exotic species.

From our tropic shore we watched the barracuda
cross the panoramic window of the breaking wave,
gazed on coral reefs where parrot fish would ape
the sergeant majors' nibbling drill,
and Prospero's son glimpsed his father weave
the dreams he heard in shells, holding them holy.
Then, adopting to the island's pace,
hand in hand we combed the tidal margins.

> Without you now on Newlyn's pebble beach,
> I want support and search for sticks.

I know your row but not the house's number.
Some cousin's on the hill behind.
Godmother's gone. Her shop, renamed, remains.
Jack the crab and crayfish man, best friend
who should have been best man is also dead.
His factory stands beside the stream where as a boy
you fished for trout, fell, and scarred your knee.
The village tour has brought these pieces back to me.

> I see the ailing Gulf Stream
> still provides for palm trees on the green.

So, if trawlers' gulls won't call for longtails
over deep Atlantic seas, I'll still mate them.
If Cornwall's trees are unfamiliar, I'll rename them:
what might be elms become Bermuda cedars
and may-be-oaks feign pleasure to be casuarinas.
But we share an artist's light: though these bathers
don't lie down on coral sands, they still burn.
And a man who rambles finds a stick to aid him.

> Would you accept the branch I hold?
> I hesitate, but poke it in adopted soil.

DEPARTURE
Mario Abbatiello

'Are you leaving?' Nuria asked.

In the durga,
dervishes turn and whirl
their dance of the planets;
musicians play and sing
love songs to the shining one:

Lofted into a vastness, I am
where the world's sorrows dissolve,
honey-sweet.

But I still need to catch the
last ferry to Istanbul.

KEPLER 452B
Medbh McGuckian

Numbers are useless in counting anything
Like perfumed rosaries made of plumstones
Knotted in the shape of a rose. There is only
One universe at a time, the one real world
Earlier on, when we were simpler than we are
Now, is soaked through and through with time.

The roses spelled out one word – partner –
Any flashier miracle in the unsunned snow
Or the blur of summer. I remembered how
The irises' skill in clearing up after themselves
Was like shadow children against a secluded
Gate, blue snowflakes, first fat drops of thunder.

I should re-insert the moon into the narrative
Of the war. In fact, I felt like a bonfire,
Full of dull smoke, as if I were treading
The rim of a wheel burning a string
Of crudely knotted flags. Dried blood on several
Hundred candles fluttered towards the street.

Dark as those nights may have been, as the ghosts
Of pens long dead, I sat and swayed
In my drowsy conflagration, kicking the tight-
Laced city moodily behind me, step by step,
Yet not advancing an inch. The streaks
Of the sun furled up on the curtain, the brightness
    temperature.

As if my hand had been a skinless heart
Or a raw telescope for tours of the afterlife,
Sudden frosting moonmilk on a semi-infinite
Cloud, starless cores surrounding a young star.
The stale preserved breath of the dead
Who once ruled a world that now seems of no

Importance, hooded the streetlamps,
The church bells throbbing in the towers,
Guarding forgotten dumps in abandoned bases
And empty petrol tins that shuffled like claws
To possess the half empty town. I saw much
Of these scarecrow troops, the way their youth was
    humbled,

Bled grey with boredom. Young soldiers everywhere,
Standing about in shut streets on rainy Sundays,
On midnight platforms where no trains came.
They whistled and wished to be anywhere
But here. There were times when there seemed
To be no one else but these in the city,

City of expired fanaticisms and cold, closed
Lamps. Soldiers, priests and beggars, sleek
Black priests stepping like cats on a petal
As though to extinguish a match, while the afternoon
Sun sucked up the flavour of each cramped
Tree, surely the most painless way to be wakened.

Their Christ was carved from old wood
The colour of moonlight, lilies tied to his feet,
His toes already stirring, like the weight
Of the leaves on the trees, The children were
Especially quiet, my notebook was snatched
From my hand, they didn't like the look of it,

Sniffed at, shaken, thumped hard, held upside
Down. I was pretending to be a ghost,
My face stroked by the lighthouse with
Its own grey roof of weather, and every scrap
Of old cloth run up on a pole. I had ridden
Wrapped up in a Union Jack to protect me

From the sun, and when I rolled out of it,
I felt that I was born. Or feeling well for once,
Here and there, beginning with a window
And a streak of wind letting in the sky,
Drawn by some need every evening to look
Out to sea, not knowing what my prayer should be.

Abusers of the flag have no arm to cling to.
I had to wrestle with just such an angel,
Stout angel in black dress, not an agreeable saint,
The whole poise of the evening. Not long ago
We exited a century, like prisoners of a language
Learned against our will – now every thing breathes
     2016.

As if the body needs to re-think the river
Of the world-otherwise story before it
Comes home. It is not certain that a bee
In his tapestries can hear this honey-
Centred hum with his flight muscles
Brushing it away like a bell for sleep.

PROSE

SPIRITS OF THE STONE
Martin Cromie

I keep a stone on my desk. It is a pyramid of winter grey granite, about six inches high. It comes from the ruins of my father's one-storey, two-roomed house in the Townland of Ballinliss, on the slopes of Camlough Mountain. Its edges are sharp, the sides sandpaper-rough and the base is weathered smooth and oiled dark with sweat from the hands that have touched it. When I rotate the stone in the light, each facet glints a unique arrangement of mica crystals like clusters of little stars pulsating life from the dark core of granite. I see them as bright reminders of all the lives lived in this place. To me they are like spirits of the stone.

I imagine this lump of granite being plucked from the boggy earth by an ancestor dressed in eighteenth-century peasant rags, his back aching, his arms deadened, and his hands calloused from humping rock and arranging walls and shaping a house on a flat bit of land sliced in the mountainside. I see his thick fingers slot the stone into the wall over the flat-edged heft of granite lintel that squares off an open-hearth fireplace. My mind struggles to comprehend the life of this stone before the building of the house: raised from the seabed 400 million years ago by crunching tectonic plates; blasted to the surface 60 million years ago during Slieve Gullion's volcanic eruption; gouged from the mountain 10,000 years ago under a thick glacier; dropped by the melting ice and left undisturbed for millennia, exposed to the wind, rain, frost and sun that broke and shaped it into the pyramid I know. It is at once an inanimate piece of matter and a vibrant living portal to my ancestry. It has witnessed all the lives spent on the five-acre site of my father's house from its earliest settlement to the day he abandoned it.

I imagine the stone in the cold darkness of winter and the long warm light of summer, in the presence of intimate conversations or late night gatherings, when stories were told, and family myths created and enlarged. I consider the wakes, weddings, and births this stone has attended. And I wonder how many generations of hands have touched its hard surface, how many of my ancestors have warmed themselves at the fire in the hearth. I like to think of my father reaching up to the stone as a child. Maybe he gave it a fond caress on that day in 1954, when, having given up any hope of making a living on a poor mountain farm, he left his home for the final time.

Around the stone, my desk is strewn with the bric-a-brac of family history. Faces stare at me from photographs. I sift through copies of handwritten census returns and valuation books. I notice that in 1864 eight of the sixty-four plots in the townland of Ballinliss are in the name of Cromie or Crummie or Crommie, depending on the whim of the census taker or the valuator. Unravelling the connections reminds me of a childhood comic puzzle in which three cartoon figures each holds a string attached to one of three balloons floating above them. The strings are tangled and intertwined. The object of the puzzle is to identify which character holds which balloon. I trace the twists and turns of the strings, frustrated at failed attempts then smugly satisfied when I eventually match characters and balloons. As I dig through my notes and pore over the copperplate handwriting in the copied documents, my experience is more often one of failed attempts rather than smug satisfaction. And into this puzzle is added the genealogical complications of my grandparents' marriage certificate which records Catherine (Kitty) Cromie of Ballinliss marrying Stephen Cromie of Ballintemple in 1907. Cromie married to Cromie. For the superstitious this would have endowed Kitty with the cure for whooping cough, an old wives' tale that can't be substantiated. But neither can it be disproven. And where proof is elusive, myth is nurtured. Like family history.

Old Ordnance Survey maps add to the confusion since my father's house is clearly plotted at the end of the loanan in the mid 1830s and yet the Valuation Revision books only recognise its existence in 1903. Is this the result of human error, a scribe's oversight? Or is there a rational explanation which reconciles the haze of impressions I have inherited from my family and the meticulously detailed records entered in the ledgers of surveyors? One snippet of fact, a date, a detail, leads to something else, and before long a logical pathway becomes a maze of tangents that usher me into unknown territories. I am not a genealogist, yet untangling the breadth and depth of documented ancestral connections suddenly becomes an obsession. Nor am I a historian, but since the story of my family is wedded to the history of this mountain landscape, I immerse myself in its historical and archaeological narratives.

Writing helps me make sense of this journey into the landscape and to understand why a ruined cottage on a mountainside holds such an attraction for me. And, since the writing reflects the journey, there is an inevitable wandering and wondering, digression and diversion in the directions in which my words seem to take me. By nature, I am inclined towards the security of a plan and the comfort of props – map, compass, signposts and well maintained paths. Instead I find myself going where the spirits take me in a figurative and literal sense, on a journey of discovery wherein something new is found in the landscape and in me. It is a physical journey: walking, following maps, and re-tracing the footsteps of my father. But it is also a metaphysical expedition into the landscape and through time, unearthing facts, dispelling myths, clarifying what had been thought to be true. I find myself delayering the collective memory of family, stripping back the recorded landscape, comparing revisions in a century of Ordnance Survey maps, studying the colour-coded rock variations displayed on geological maps and delving into the lives of ancient people documented in archaeological surveys. The history of people and place entangle like rampant ivy laced through the cracks in drystone walls.

I unfurl an old six-inch Ordnance Survey map. Townlands are outlined in feint red. Those of my father's people are arrayed left to right from Ballintemple to Tamnaghbane, Ballinliss and Ballymacdermot. The boundaries follow roads and paths, sheughs and ditches, streams and hedges that separate one townland from the next. Bench Marks dot the landscape. BM 591.3 is near the loanan to my father's house. In 1830 Major General Thomas Colby, director of the Ordnance Survey, established a baseline benchmark on the shores of Lough Foyle in County Derry from where a swathe of Royal Engineers mapped the physical features of every inch of Ireland, moving systematically north to south. Richard Griffith, a civilian engineer, led another team of surveyors who plotted the boundaries of every townland and parish. On the map in front of me the benchmark plots the spot where a sapper might have stood with a theodolite and blue-backed journal, recording levels across the fields around my father's home. He might have seen my great-great-grandfather, Francis, hoking spuds from the ground or rounding up sheep on the mountainside. And later one of Griffith's men might have been seen hopping stone walls, following the run of a stream, or the length of a cart-rutted lane, laying down a sixty-six foot measuring chain and establishing forever the precise entity of Ballinliss. Perhaps he sat with his back against the drystone wall, drawing board on his knee, penning his findings, glancing occasionally across the field, smelling the turf fire and the sweet whiff of griddle bread on the breeze.

These men knew the landscape through the intricacy of numbers: its heights, distances, acreages and value. My father's people knew it too, but through the intimacy of living and working, breeding and dying on it. They knew it stone by stone, field by field, and season by season. The pyramid of granite on the desk is my benchmark. Its facets remind me of Colby's mathematical triangulation. And if I stand in front of the ruins of my father's house and cast a theodolite eye from east to west, I can pick out the unique characteristics of this place and feel a connection to my father among its stone walls and fields. Sometimes the connection is tangible like the solid stone in front of me. More often it is ethereal: flattened grass in the lee of a wall where my father sat posing for a photograph seventy years ago; the sharp pips of his penny whistle carried on the wind from Seaver's Road where the jigs and reels of summer ceilidhs once seeped out of

Ballinliss Hall; or the rattle of his bike free-wheeling the Bernish hill, its mudguards clattering with every bump on the rock pocked road. According to the poet Paul Farley, Welsh writers use the word *Wireath* to describe an anguished sense of separation from places we love. It is a home-sickness of sorts, for which the only cure is to go back and to know that this is the place from whence you came. A place like this is not just a set of coordinates on a map: it is a web of connections in the head and the heart; it is where you will encounter the spirits of the stone.

GOING HOME
Maurice Savage

His footsteps echoed through the cavernous multi-storey car park. It was virtually empty at that late hour. He walked through the cold towards the main doors of the hospital; he passed through the vacant reception area, and headed for the lift. The machinery groaned as it came to a stop.

'Third-floor, Oncology and Haematology,' announced a lifeless, robotic voice.

His heart heavy, he walked down the hallway and stopped outside the door. He thought about the phone call he had received a few hours earlier, which had diverted him from returning to the warmth and comfort of home. He would not be reading bedtime stories to his daughters tonight. Entering the room quietly, he stood for a moment as his eyes adjusted to the gloom. He registered the green glow of the cardiac monitor. His own heart was pounding, his eyes stinging. The skin on his neck and arms prickled.

Eithne lay still on the bed, her eyes closed. She was held in comfort by crisp, white sheets. In the dim light of the anglepoise lamp, her skin looked white, her lips pale. Her breathing was almost imperceptible, but she seemed strangely peaceful as she slept. He became aware that her mother and father were rising to their feet behind him. He turned towards them and involuntarily stretched out his hands. Clare stepped into his arms. They held onto each other in shared grief. He raised his eyes and looked over her shoulder at Sean, the big strong man who stood there, for once looking helpless. He held out his right hand to him, and it was warmly taken in the farmer's strong, rough grip. Tears spilled down the visitor's unshaven face.

'She said you would come,' Sean whispered.

His throat was so dry and painful, that at first he could not speak. He shook his head, searching for words. He knew that Eithne's stepfather loved her as much as anyone loved his own, and more than the father she had possibly never known.

'You know how fond she was of you,' Sean said, as if reading his thoughts.

Again he struggled to reply.

'She was always a very special little girl to me,' he managed to say at last. 'She didn't say a lot to me when she was very small, and she rarely complained – not about blood tests, not about operations, I think she only cried when she wanted to go home. We got to know each other so well as time went by. But when she got older, and I had to scold her because I knew she wasn't taking her tablets, she could turn on a good sulk. I hoped she understood it was because we cared about her so much.'

Clare quickly interjected: 'She never held it against you when you were cross. She would never have admitted it, but in her own way she looked forward to coming up to the clinic in Belfast – especially when she felt so well after getting her new kidney.'

They stood together looking at Eithne, now a young woman; each had memories of her. The visitor thought of the baby girl with the curly brown hair, her dark green eyes that spoke even before she could utter many words. He thought of the night he found her mum wrapped round her, the two of them sleeping in the big, metal hospital cot. He thought of the schoolgirl, proud of her new uniform. He recalled the brave teenager, passionate about music, who stoically faced weeks of chemotherapy. He felt anger and despair at how unfair life could be.

He tried to lighten the moment.

'She wasn't too pleased when I vetoed her having her ears pierced because of the risk of infection with the drugs she was taking,' he said.

'Nor when you said an eyebrow ring wasn't a great idea,' said Clare, with a little smile. 'Then she came up with the idea of a nose stud. She was just being a normal fourteen-year-old, enjoying winding us up.'

'She beat us all in the end,' added Sean. 'More power to her. I'll never forget the look on your face when she pulled down the neck of her shirt, to show you that tattoo of Michael Jackson's face on her shoulder! That was one of her last visits to the children's clinic. That was when I discovered how big a fan she was, and actually it was a superb likeness.'

A little voice came from the bed.

'You said I had got too big for the outpatient Wendy house.'

The old, cheeky smile flickered on her face. The visitor walked over, and sat down on her bed, wondering how long she'd been listening.

'I've been waiting for you to come and see me,' she said.

Gently, he took her right hand with a smile. 'Was I your favourite patient then?' she asked, as she used to.

'Doctors aren't allowed favourites,' he answered, as always. Their eyes met and he leaned over to kiss her forehead then whispered in her ear, 'Yes, of course you were.' Soon Eithne's hand slipped from his. Sean and Clare sat down on the other side of her bed. Just then a kindly ward auxiliary quietly looked in.

'I've got some tea and biscuits next door,' she said.

They sat sipping the tasteless hospital brew, recalling good days and tough days they had shared when Eithne was a child. They also thought about all she had been through in recent months.

Eventually the visitor said, 'No matter what happens, she has known nothing but love from you and her brothers and sister.' He paused, then added: 'Let's go back in and see her again. Then I should leave you with her and head home.'

As they stood, Clare turned to him, and said, 'She's

not going to make it this time is she?'

The choking ache was back in his throat.

'No, I don't think so,' he said sadly.

'She knows that,' said Sean, with a weak smile, 'and she was sure you'd come.'

KEEPING A DIARY FOR MY MOTHER
Shelley Tracey

3rd July 1985 – In the lounge

It's been a long time since supper. The clock is stuttering, with each separate tick coming after a long breath. Pa and I are in the lounge, not saying anything, as usual, but I think he likes my company. The TV is on but the sound is off. I don't think he's watching anything. He's just staring at the screen. I think if the old test pattern came on as it used to when we first got TV, he would stare at that too. His coffee is on the arm of his chair, but I don't think he's drunk any of it. He said 'thank you' when I made it for him, and let me stir it as I used to when I was small, but all he did was just put it down next to him. He is staring straight ahead, motionless like a lizard glued in place by the heat. I don't think he has even noticed me writing. I can hear the faint brush of the side of my hand across the page, the beetle scratches of the pen, and the slow march of the clock.

Since Ma has been in hospital, time has slowed down so much that I notice everything: every pattern on the carpet and the way they connect with each other, every smear on the copper jugs and bowls on the coffee table, and every little noise. The sound of the crickets in the evening is not just in the background anymore. Now I am aware of the smallest details: the tiny shrill notes and crescendos, and the pauses between each 'chreep, chreep, chreep'. I'm not sure if it's my imagination, but I think I can even hear the crickets moving up the stubby blades of kikuyu grass. How many of them are there out there? Are they calling to each other, or are they all singing a song they have known for millennia?

Ma and I like going out at night to look at the stars. She loves that about South Africa; she says you can see many more stars here than in England, especially in dark country places like our farm. These days I think I hear the stars communicating with each other. I know they are millions of miles away, but I can imagine the sizzles and sparks they make. There are so many stars, and they are connected in constellations and galaxies, so they must have their own languages and ways of letting each other know they are there.

Ma and I used to have our own way of speaking to each other without words. Every single time I go to see her in hospital, I feel sure she is going to open her eyes and say something to me. Her face is frozen in a look as if she is about to tell me something really important. I wonder what it is? I wonder if she even knows she had a baby? I wonder if she wants to ask me about him or about Pa?

It's too quiet in the hospital ward; it feels as if we are two prisoners in adjoining cells, both in solitary confinement, not allowed to speak to each other. The connection between us, mother and daughter, so many jokes and conversations, has vanished. I hold Ma's hand for a bit, just in case it makes her remember how she held my hand when I was a little girl. But it's like holding dead twigs – narrow bony ones like Hansel poked out of his cage to make the witch think he was too thin to eat.

The blankness in Ma's silence makes me notice the breathing machines and the ticking of something which is taking the place of her heartbeat. It's the same as at home. Time stretches and the passing of every minute draws my attention. Maybe it's a good thing; my mind becomes as lazy and blurred as if I am catching a tan on the beach, and I stop worrying about things. I look at the flowers in her ward and I count the petals. Today I saw that someone had brought in bronze and white and yellow chrysanthemums. Ma hates chrysanthemums. We have a private joke about them, how they are almost as bad as artificial flowers, because they look so sad and lifeless. But today they were something to look at and pass the time. I imagined all the ways I could describe them to Ma when she wakes up. I thought of skinny daisies, which have been kept indoors for too long, or moulting mossies, with their drip, drip, drip of boring beige petals. It's was quite strange how my mind started to wander.

Last week Pa brought home some of the proteas he bought for Ma and we put them in the lounge. They are still here in a vase, turning to paper. The water is green and slimy. I wish I had the energy to throw them away, but I can't imagine pouring something that reminds me of Ma down the sink and losing sight of the last drop of her.

When you move anything on the tables and other surfaces in this room, there is a furry dust circle underneath it. For the first time, I notice how many ashtrays there are. Ma used to gather them up after we had visitors and let them soak, but there is always a trace of grey ash that never completely disappears, no matter how hard you scrub it. Under Ma's chair there is still a yellow plastic bag with her knitting. She made a few little jerseys while she was expecting Boetie, but she found it hard to finish them. 'It's too hot,' she used to say; 'the needles make my hands feel sweaty.' A ball of pale yellow wool is poking out of the bag like a toy that's losing its stuffing.

Pa still hasn't said anything. I wonder if the clock has stopped. I am starting to learn that there is a big difference between the silence of feeling relaxed, and the silence of waiting, not knowing if things are ever going to be the same again. Sometimes I think to myself, well, I am fifteen years old, and my life ended when my mother got sick. What if there is nothing good to look forward to?

THE MEMORY TREE
Emma Kane

I slowed down as I drove past the house where I grew up, straining my neck as I went by, as I always did. I am not at all sure what, if anything, I expected to see, but the big old house surrounded by trees had always been the closest thing to home I could ever remember. All my childhood memories revolved around that house, and each time I found myself in the area I went out of my way to pass it, indulging myself in feelings of nostalgia. I had lived there as an only child with my parents up to the age of eleven, before being shipped off to boarding school on the North Coast, after which life was different. My leaving seemed to trigger a fracture within the family, which led to everything breaking. My parents split up, and our beautiful Edwardian home was sold, along with every stick of quaint, antiquated furniture in it. The horses were sold too, like they were inanimate objects. The family dog, a bad-breathed furry old Alsatian named O'Reilly died of old age, or so I was told. The dog had looked after me from the age of two: we had grown up together. One day I arrived home from school for the holidays and it was all gone. I often wondered what I missed most. For what seemed like an age after that we didn't seem to have a home. I stayed with aunts and cousins in the summers and at Christmas. From that day to this, wherever I resided never felt like home. I had spent my entire adult life feeling like a nomad, never really settling anywhere for very long.

As I passed the old house a 'For Sale' sign caught my eye. I slammed on the brakes and reversed up the centre of the quiet road. Apprehensive and excited, I pulled into the driveway. My mind was connecting the dots. It must be empty, I thought. Maybe I could find a way in so I could look around? I just wanted a peek. I peered through the dining room window and was surprised to see the same twenty-year-old wallpaper staring back at me. Feeling like a criminal I crept around the side of the house until I reached the back door. With anticipation I turned the handle, and was surprised to find the door unlocked. As I pushed it gently it creaked open to reveal the kitchen, almost exactly as it had looked when I was eleven years old. I stepped inside, feeling as though I had stumbled into a familiar dream. Placing the palm of my hand on the icy cold wall steeped in memories, I closed my eyes. Visions of my childhood flooded back. A sepia-tinted scene of my mother, young, smiling, carving the Christmas turkey, appeared before me. At the opposite end of the room was my father, plunked in his favourite armchair, his nose in a newspaper. He was resting his bare feet on the back of O'Reilly. As I moved through the house it seemed smaller than I remembered. It had appeared huge when I was little. It seemed as though it had shrunk, or maybe I had simply grown; but it provoked a feeling of disappointment in me.

Nervously, I made my way upstairs. Reaching the top of the first flight I came to my parents' bedroom. The door was shut, as it had always been to me. With the renewed confidence that comes with age, I pushed open the door and brazenly entered the room. My head reeled. I recalled the night I had followed the sound of my mother's laughter into this room, only to be pushed out by a red-faced, barely clothed father. I remembered the morning my mother's screams had called me to this room, only to be guided out by a nice lady in a nurse's uniform, but not before I had caught a glimpse of a strange man holding a tiny baby who was blue in colour and made no sound. That was the closest I ever got to having a sibling. Then came the recollection of an afternoon when a strange silence had drawn me to this room, like a magnet. I recalled the static feeling in the air as I wondered where my mother was. I remembered shaking her, and feeling fear and confusion overcome me when I couldn't rouse her. I recalled an image of myself as a little girl, kneeling on the floor to pick up the pills strewn about her bed, and putting them back into the bottle. Backing out of that room, I wondered about the happy times.

On entering my old bedroom, I quickly realised I had no affinity with this room at all. Searching my memories, it dawned on me that I had never played in here, but merely slept. I felt the pull towards the window. I gazed out at the overgrown garden, drinking in its beauty. The garden called me, and I had no desire to look around the rest of the house. I was outside in seconds, and the girl I had been came alive. I kicked off my shoes, revelling in the feel of the damp grass beneath my feet. A slow smile of contentment crept over my face. I was a child again, lying on my belly in the wet earth, peering into the dark, muggy water of the pond. I waited with quiet anticipation, hoping to catch a glimpse of a slimy, bouncing, croaking frog. I turned onto my back and lay gazing at the sky, a beautiful tumbling cascade of blue, with no beginning and no end – a stark contrast to life. Then I caught sight of the old oak tree; like an old friend awaiting my return, it seemed to beckon me. I stroked its rough bark as if it were velvet, and with complete disregard for my linen trousers I began to climb. Once aloft, I paused and listened to the birds sing their familiar song and I marvelled at the feeling that time had stood still. The smell of grass, bark and earth filled my nostrils. I lay there among the branches of my old friend, feeling safe and cared for. Cradled by the tree, for the first time in over twenty years, I felt like I was home.

LANDAGIVEY HOUSE
Toni Bradley

Having always been used to London street names and house numbers, it seemed that we were now to live in a house with a name. My ten-year-old self envisaged grandeur and luxury, a place the Famous Five would have liked to investigate. And grand it would turn out to be, though not quite as I imagined. I would grow to realise that nothing in life quite matched my expectations but, like Landagivey, would often surprise me in different ways.

Crammed between my older sister and younger brother in the front of the delivery van, we followed the long-neglected lane to the old dilapidated house, only identified as a working farm by the adjoining barns and the absence of a back garden. It boasted neither electricity nor inside plumbing. To the side of the house, shaded by a cypress tree, stood a Victorian pump which would serve us for several months.

The house still retained the trappings of a past love. Now, in late summer, the abandoned garden nurtured rhododendron bushes and glorious multi-shaded hydrangeas; the uncut lawns were strewn with escaping azalea blossoms, the apple trees bowed with unpicked fruit. A wooden bench, cracked and weathered racing green, had been thoughtfully placed before the house, its elegant wrought-iron fixtures harking back to better days. The hedges beyond the garden were ripe with sloes. By spring there would be baby chicks in the outhouse, bikes in the shed, goats in the garden, another baby in the pram, and a donkey in the side field. The boggy, flat farmland would support – or, on occasion, submerge – the young heifers my father bought. But that was all ahead of us. First the house needed to be brought to heel.

Inside was a large kitchen with a walk-in pantry that suggested a time when a scullery maid would have skivvied and scrubbed alongside the farmer's wife to feed all hands. Back then the shelves would have been autumn-laden with jams and preserves to last the winter mouths. It was built for self-sufficiency, not for this family of city folk who had left their claustrophobic semi, with its dry square of back garden, its black and white telly and its washing machine. Apart from our father's stories the only knowledge we had of farm life and rearing cattle came from watching *Rawhide* on TV.

Pride of the kitchen was the range, a Rayburn Royal, cream-enamelled and radiating a dry heat that warmed this large, draughty hub of our home. My mother's first experience of cooking without gas led to a prolonged period of burnt potatoes and buttermilk-sodden wheaten bread. It would be mastered by the time winter set in, when my father would catch hares in traps and we would watch him skin them for casseroles, cooked slowly in the stove.

The living room floor was covered in a green substance called tintawn, a post-war invention that was a poor man's substitute for a carpet. When you got up from the nightly rosary, it left on your knees an impression like a blank crossword, which stayed there until the next night's torture.

That first summer my sister, Mary, was to get her long-promised puppy. I got a tyre suspended from a spreading oak and would swing for hours with my little brother, playing pirates and sailors, glorying in the space and freedom, with the donkey watching from the adjacent field.

On Tuesdays the mobile grocer would arrive. It was the highlight of the week for me, and the only glimpse of the bounty we had left behind. For my mother the link with civilisation was the mobile library, which came once a fortnight. It would park along the 'New Line' some two miles away. She would send me there in an eager search for escapism in the words of Pearl Buck or Nevil Shute.

All of this was accepted as the way things were, like everything else in childhood. The lowland of the Agivey basin was sodden and poor; the farm holding was small. Our parents didn't precisely make bad choices, but we were gradually drifting into a country poverty that was a colder and more desolate condition than life lived in the city. When they faced a mounting pile of unpaid bills we would all do extra time at the rosary, down on our knees on the tintawn, secure in the belief that God would provide. By the time October came it was hoped that help had arrived. The potato harvest in a neighbouring farm was due in. My parents gladly offered up Mary and me for a Saturday's picking. The promise of earning ten shillings each, with a shilling of our own to keep, made us delirious with excitement. We had inherited our parents' capacity for novelty and self-belief. Potato picking – how hard could it be?

The day started cold and early, and we crawled our way through sticky mud and stubborn potatoes that had to be individually prised from the chill clay. In our village school there were only two classes, so I knew the ages of all the other children at the gathering. They and their younger siblings trudged and chatted as they picked and plopped and carried to the waiting tractors. Mary and I were soon left far behind as we struggled down our drill.

A whistle called us to lunch and we entered the farmhouse kitchen to be served by old Mrs MacDonald. We were greeted with a plate of water-logged potatoes and a blob of sour-smelling country butter. I had an aching back, hands torn to shreds, and a realisation that work, especially hard work, was not what God had intended for me. Mary could, and did, stay, but I cried off with a phoney tummy upset. No shilling for me as I headed home to the security of Landagivey. Here I was greeted by my mother with some warmth and understanding, by my father with disappointment and shame. But the greatest damage caused by my failure to pass this most basic of country tests would be suffered back in the school yard.

Children didn't just turn up at St. Luke's Primary School: they were expected for generations. They could be seen coming down the line from a long way off. They carried no mysteries. From the filling in their sandwiches to the weight of their brains, everything was as it should be. I arrived with a strong Home Counties accent and an education some level beyond the rest of Primary Seven. While the teacher looked at me with some interest, the pupils saw me as a threat to the way things had always been. Like any pack animals, they sniffed and they watched, they tested and they plotted. I was a big girl, well nourished, and strong – despite my failure in the potato field. I rode my mother's bike well to school. I would be hard to catch. Not so my brother, little Joe. At five years old he had all the naïvety he was born with.

He would ride alongside me over the old runway, the shortcut to and from school. The long stretch of tarmac was part of a base used by the American forces during the Second World War and still strewn with old huts and tarred pathways. Its greatest attraction was a drawing on one of the walls, of a kneeling woman identified as 'Jayne', with long flowing hair and head tilted back, flaunting her huge naked breasts at us. She was like a deity, so much more exciting than the timid Virgin Mary. Such power and arrogance; such nipples! How I longed to be her. Joe and I would seek her out every afternoon on our way home from school.

One afternoon as we left her shrine to ride homewards our path was blocked by three girls from my class carrying sticks. These were children fed with tales of a subjugated Ireland, who were now emboldened by thoughts of beating the English. Little Joe and I, with our outgrown clothes and rusty bikes, still represented the oppressors. I sensed the threat.

I yelled at Joe to keep cycling and, letting out every oath I knew – 'bloody' and 'hell' and 'damn' – I charged through them on my bike. But Joe wasn't following. They had pulled him off his bike, stabilisers still spinning, and had him gripped tightly. That meant I had to go in and through their lashings in order to reach him. These weren't violent children, and it didn't last long. Their sticks were merely props for terrorising, not weapons for mauling. We were soon allowed back on our bikes with the taunt 'Sassenachs go home'. This was more about showing me my place than beating me to death. I learnt quickly. I kept my mouth shut in class and my hand well down, I no longer sang 'Rule Britannia' at the top of my voice in the playground.

I avoided the old base, and went home to Landagivey the long way. I would never see Aerodrome Jayne again and, sadly, neither would I get her big breasts.

MY SCARLET PIMPERNEL
Eilish Fleming

I remember a rather anxious occasion when I had to go with my mother to the hospital because she had fallen and cut her right leg badly. The 'bleach man' had just been. He used to come round the streets with his handcart, selling bottles of strong-smelling bleach. The bottles came in all shapes and sizes, and he collected your empties each time he called. My mum had bought three bottles and had placed them at the bottom of our stairs. She forgot they were there, tripped over and gashed her leg. The bleach had spilled out onto her. All I could see was blood! It was 1949 and I was the baby in the house. Our Patsy was in school, and I loved it because when she was there I went everywhere alone with my mum. But this was one trip I wasn't looking forward to.

We left our house, and set off down Balaclava Street, then onto Raglan Street, into Leeson Street, along Abercorn Street North, into Sorella Street, past Dunville Park, across the Grosvenor Road and into the RVH. I remember every detail of that journey because I was worried about what would happen to my mum. We went into the Royal Hospital through the archway and past Queen Victoria's statue. I can still remember the smell of the hospital – the awful reek of disinfectant. The chairs in the Royal were wooden and you could easily hurt yourself on them.

When it was my mum's turn she was brought into a room to be treated. The nurses helped her by cleaning and dressing the wound. I remember my mum lying on the bed, and I was standing in the corner looking at her, feeling like a lost soul. Her leg was bandaged from the knee to the ankle, and I felt frightened because I couldn't help her. Everyone was so busy that they didn't have time for little children.

Suddenly a nurse pulled back the curtain, and called out, 'It's him!'

All the staff and patients began to shout and cheer. I didn't know what was happening. Then the man who caused the disturbance – a medical student – waltzed in. He turned to face me, lifted me up, and put me on a chair. At this small gesture the crowd cheered even louder. I didn't understand any of it: why were they cheering this man? And who was he anyway?

Much later I discovered that it was Jack Kyle, the rugby fly-half, who had led Ireland to their first-ever Grand Slam. The papers called him 'The Scarlet Pimpernel' because he was so elusive. When I recall it now I think that it was such a wonderful thing for him to do; in the midst of all that excitement this sporting legend took the time to make a frightened little girl feel better.

At that time I was five, and thought Kyle was at least ten feet tall; but I now know that he wasn't really very big at all. I watched him on television in 2008, and he was a tiny, old man then; but I was still very impressed by him because I remembered every detail of that day when I encountered this legend. I also learned he was a devout Christian: this was evident in his good deeds. He worked as a medical missionary in Zambia for 34 years. In 2002 the Irish RFU voted him the island's greatest-ever player. He received a lifetime achievement award from the Royal Academy of Medicine in Ireland, and died in 2014. I'm sorry I never got to say thanks to this wonderful man, but I am so proud to be able to say I met the 'Scarlet Pimpernel' in person.

BALLYMURPHY
Angie Creighton

I hope that by writing wee stories about growing up in 'the Murph' I am not offending anyone. I posted a story online recently, and Facebook took it off; for what reason I have no idea. So for the next wee snippet I apologise in advance, if certain people take it in the wrong context. You see, I don't look back in time through rose-tinted glasses. I remember pain, heartache and happiness. It's how my family, and my Ballymurphy family (love yas xx) dealt with things, how they lived and worked together. Looking back, they were, and still are, amazing people.

We lived by, and adhered to, the rules of the Catholic Church. We went to Mass, believed sex before marriage was a sin, and that it was unforgivable to miss going to church. Almost every house had pictures of the Pope and President John F. Kennedy, and in our house there was holy water at every doorway. Blessing ourselves was a habit, and was believed to be effective in keeping the Devil out. The priest used to call round weekly for a chat and, of course, to ensure that we were all attending services. My daddy never had any time for priests or religion; he believed that the Church was to blame for poverty, and he said that during the Famine he was sure there were no starving priests. So the priests' visits to our house weren't frequent, as my daddy put them out. My mammy was always looking for answers. You see, in our house my family had to face the most inconceivable pain (which I will write about another time). My parents dealt with things in whatever way they could. My mammy came back from Mass one Sunday and told of how the priest had asked us to put notes instead of coins in the envelopes. My daddy said, 'Well what did I tell you? They'll never starve.' After that mammy's visits to church were less frequent. You see, the way my daddy saw it, it was all about control.

At school some of the teachers would victimise us because of where we came from. There were kids in our class who were better off than we were, and the teachers would bring them to the front and would be more attentive to their educational needs. One of my classmates had a father who was a policeman, and she was always given preferential treatment. The teachers were always quick to put the needs of these students before the rest of us.

At secondary school there could have been ten kids misbehaving, and if one of the kids was from 'the Murph', her punishment would be severe – more so than the rest. The teachers used to say, 'Sure is it any wonder! Look at where they come from. What do you expect?' One time my mammy went down and told them I wasn't going back, because of their treatment of us Ballymurphy kids.

Once, when my friends were playing a basketball match in another district the locals threw things at them and were abusive about their appearance. This wasn't banter; it was victimisation, hooliganism. Anyway our team won, and they had to run like the hammers or they would have been lynched.

A friend once told me that his father told him about this lovely girl he met from Ballymurphy, and when his parents found out they told him to dump her. Horrible – and they hadn't even met her! But he didn't dump her, and 50 odd years later they're still happily married.

My daddy's nightly ritual was to sit by the fire with a mug of stewed tea while eating the heel of a plain loaf. He would scrutinise every inch of the newspaper. I remember how he once turned to mammy and said, 'Peggy, wait till ya see this! Some a**hole has been spewing rubbish!' He was fuming, with my mammy sitting beside him, reading the article out loud. The reporter had written a derogatory article about how run down the place where we lived was, and went on about the state of the people. In fact he said we were like animals. As far as I'm aware he didn't speak to anyone in the district. The reporter didn't mention that there was severe unemployment, and the infant mortality rate was high. He was opinionated, and as far as I'm concerned, should have been sacked. However another set of reporters read the story. They were curious and sent their own team in to investigate 'these people, these animals.' They interviewed local families and, I'm told, did their homework, and their account was an honest one and totally different. (I'm looking into finding these accounts, as I remember the article and am trying to find the BBC's one.)

We faced class discrimination, religious discrimination and a war. I am so proud of where I come from – a place where I made lifelong friendships and gained life skills from my parents and neighbours. It's a community that I treasure and feel blessed for having.

TORNAGROUGH
Pauline Brady

Tornagrough! Even now the very name itself sounds magical. I chant it over and over in my head and I am transported back through the years to those innocent days of childhood when everything seemed simpler and more pleasant, to that hedgerowed lane where I had many magical rambles. During the long summer holidays I would walk there daily, a 'townie' savouring the sights, sounds and smells of the unspoilt countryside. As I entered the lane my nostrils were first assaulted by the pungent smell of wild garlic, quickly followed by the fetid fumes of cow dung rising in the air and competing with the other odours for pungency. These smells were alien to my town-bred senses, but I never found them unpleasant. I relished the different sights and smells and delighted in the peacefulness of the scenery.

On those wonderful summer days, as I walked along the lane, my eyes would be drawn to the bramble bushes filled with blackberries bursting with juice that stained and sweetened my mouth. I never minded the prick of the thorns of the stinging nettles that scratched and pockmarked my legs as I stretched to pick the next piece of ripe fruit. A docken leaf would soon take away the sting and leave its green stains on the offended limb. It was a pleasant fifteen-minute walk to the river above, but it often took me longer as I stopped to climb the old sycamore tree and gaze around the countryside below me. I loved to sing 'The Green Glens of Antrim' as I took my time wandering up the well-worn path. Bees would be buzzing busily in the honeysuckle bushes. I loved to inhale the sweetness from the flower's bell-shaped mouth. It was the place where I heard my first corncrake growl out its distinctive call and where I heard the curlew's cry: a strange, plaintive echo of its name.

I was very much into the *Anne of Green Gables* series of books at that time, and often imagined myself to be that girl, dreaming of her future loves and life experiences; I was a real country girl at heart. I could make all the obvious and subtle connections between myself and the heroine of Montgomery's books. Like Anne I was a redheaded eleven-year-old girl. Unlike Anne I was not an orphan, sent by mistake to live in a farmhouse with an elderly brother and sister; but I was parted from my family and sent to stay with my Aunt Sheila and Uncle John to keep them company and work on their farm. Like Anne I had a temper and sometimes got into silly, childhood moods and scrapes. I imagined myself in the future, like my much-admired heroine, changing from the awkward, ugly duckling to a beautiful, intelligent swan.

Arriving at the river, after plodding through the sodden fields spattered with cows' clap, was always an exhilarating experience. I would throw myself down on the grass and lean over to sip the cool, clear water as it made its way down from the Black Mountain, rippling and rolling over the stones. On many occasions my siblings and I would bathe in that sparkling water and my brothers would hook out fish with small sticks. Often we all would picnic at the side of the river on sunny, summer Sundays when the entire family had made the long walk to Tornagrough up the winding Hannahstown Hill, stopping briefly at Charlie Watters' pub to drink the refreshing water from the tap outside. It's funny to think about it now, but the water in the country tasted so much nicer. I loved to drink the water at my Uncle John's farmhouse. It came from a well that he had singlehandedly dug out up the fields, as he had done with other wells on other land in those parts.

I remember one day in particular, when walking in the fields with my uncle, we came across a dead cow half-eaten by maggots. I was sickened beyond belief by the revolting sight and the horrible stench that emanated from the rotting corpse. They were the images in my nightmares for weeks afterwards, and the vision has remained vivid in my memory all these years later. John, as always, took it in his stride. He was a real character, a true countryman, ever unfazed by the sights and sounds of life and death. The words that Anne of Green Gables utters towards the end of the book remind me of John so much: 'God's in his heaven, all's right with the world.' John loved his little piece of heaven. He never holidayed or travelled anywhere except to walk to

Bangor or to Belfast city centre to dances when he was young. There was no need to travel to dances once he had met my aunt Sheila, a quiet, gentle soul who baked and cooked on the big range and reared his two beloved daughters while he was constantly outdoors working in all weathers.

John had no interest in material possessions. He had one suit which he purchased for his own wedding; it was taken out for funerals, but never weddings, as he didn't attend any that he was invited to. He spent his week kitted out in his old patched jeans held up with a piece of string, and his wellies, which were also patched numerous times. Once he appeared on the television programme 'Mc Gillacuddy's Way'. In this programme the interviewer travelled round the country interviewing local characters and he certainly met a fascinating local character when he interviewed Uncle John. When John was asked what he thought of the many magpies about the place he replied that he would have no hesitation in wringing their necks. John didn't drink or smoke, and lived on a simple diet of his favourite purdies with an egg, provided by his own hens, cracked over them. He rarely ate meat.

I spent the long summer days dividing my time between Sheila and John in that old farmhouse, which had an outside toilet and no electricity; they used Tilley lamps to light the way. There was no television, just an old radio set and, although I sometimes felt very lonely, away from my family and friends, I have to say that I really enjoyed my time spent there. I loved to watch Aunt Sheila bake the potato bread, and the wheaten and soda farls on the big range in the front room and – better still – to eat them warm and slathered in butter and her own home-made jam. I will never forget the days spent milking cows and collecting hens' eggs, or other days in the fields with Uncle John, piling up the hay with pitchforks (there were no machines then for baling the hay). I would ignore the blisters on my hands until the time came for John to slap his cure-all, Germolene, on them, responding to my moaning with his usual adage, 'It won't do you a hate of harm'.

There is one particular Germolene moment that stands out in my memory. John had been trailing the hay rucks down to the hayloft on the back of his little green van. Me, his nephew George and a friend of George's from the neighbourhood called Maurice were hitching a ride to the hayloft on the top of the rucks. We were laughing and whooping and having a great time until George slipped and caught his foot on one of the ropes holding the ruck in place. We shouted out to John to stop the van but he didn't. I think he thought we were just shouting and messing about as usual. Poor George was dragged on his backside the whole way to the hayloft, screaming in agony. When John stopped the van and saw what happened he was totally unsympathetic. He merely told me and Maurice to start pitching the hay up into the loft while he took George indoors to apply the proverbial Germolene to the affected area. I felt so sorry and embarrassed for George as I listened to his cries of pain while John slapped on the Germolene and told him it wouldn't do him 'a hate of harm'.

My summer evenings were spent with John walking the fields and the Black Mountain while he pointed out the flora and fauna: the bluebells, dandelions, buttercups and cuckoo spittle, the kestrel hawk which had its nest in the white cliff, the rabbits, hares and badgers. John had an abiding love for all things natural and he made some of the ordinary sights and sounds of the countryside seem extraordinary and magical to my untrained, childish eyes. John was also very territorial and often reacted in a very violent way when strangers invaded his land. During 'The Troubles' the British Army were stationed on the Black Mountain and had a firing range there, and one day John happened across a foot patrol walking in his fields. John had a spade in his hand, as he often did, and ran at the soldiers, brandishing the spade and ordering them to get off his land. The soldiers responded by training their rifles on him and telling him they could walk 'where they effing well liked'. Undaunted, John reminded them in no uncertain terms that they 'were on Johnny Hannon's land and had no right to be there uninvited'. For some strange reason the soldiers didn't become more aggressive, as I had seen them do before in other situations; they simply walked off laughing and John was fit to be tied.

John had another peculiar night-time routine which he invited me to participate in. The lane leading to John's house was known in some parts of the town as Lovers' Lane. It was a particular bugbear of John's that some of the courting couples would invade his privacy by reversing their cars into his laneway to turn round to go home. As always John had a plan up his sleeve to stop this practice. He took me into the byre with him one night, placed a long plank of wood on the ground and proceeded to hammer six-inch nails up through it. He then took the wood and placed it at the entrance to his lane. He had me sitting with him in the dark to watch with pleasure as some unsuspecting Romeo drove onto John's property, only to have his tyres burst by the protruding nails. However there was one wag who was a nightly visitor to the lovers' meeting place, a middle-aged gentleman who was always dressed in a suit, and who got wise to Uncle John's tricks. I watched my Uncle John's face contort with anger as, one night, this man got out of his car, threw the plank up into the grass and proceeded to reverse his car unhindered into John's lane. The air in the room was blue as John swore his revenge on this upstart.

The next evening John took me into the byre again. He placed the plank of wood on the ground and plastered it in creosote. He then placed it on the ground and we retired indoors to watch John's new plan unfold. Sure enough the said gentleman appeared and stepped out of his car to remove the plank. As he lifted it up his face was a sight to behold, when he realised that his hands and fashionable suit were covered in creosote. John could not contain his laughter as he shook his fist at the man, shouting 'You'll not outfox Johnny Hannon.' And, of course, I was in convulsions of laughter too. What a wonderful nightly pastime for an eleven-year-old girl!

I can also recall my Uncle John deciding that he would make a path through his fields to the Black Mountain. This task would involve years of back-breaking labour for him, and he never saw the plan to fruition as, sadly, he died before he could complete it. He spent hours lifting out of the river the huge rocks and boulders which he would stack in the field to dry out. Then he would break them into small pieces and spread them out on the ground to create a path. One day while he was engrossed in his work he was approached by an uninvited official from the DOE. This man asked John if he had planning permission to build a road, and John dismissed him unceremoniously, telling him to get off his land immediately, and informing him that he didn't need permission from anyone to make access for himself on his own land. When my brother, who was a bricklayer, suggested that he could get him a loan of machinery to help him build the path, and perhaps some tarmac to finish the job, he immediately declined this offer, reminding my brother that this path would be here when he was gone and people would remember that Johnny Hannon built it with his own hands.

John was not happy about the National Trust's plans to build access roads to the Black Mountain. He felt that these plans would encourage too many 'townies' to come up and cause rack and ruin to the natural environment, and that it would spoil the pleasure and excitement of walking untrodden paths and finding your own way about the place. I went out the other Saturday to the Black Mountain with my sons and their children for a walk on one of those paths, and immediately thought of John and what he would be saying if he could see me and the many visitors who drive to the Divis Road car park and get out to tread these new pathways. After a pleasant walk and a picnic we called into his house, where my uncle Bobby still resides. My son was reminiscing about the great times he and his brother had when we brought them there to visit, and about the later years when they were old enough to go themselves. I looked out the window at the lane I walked so many times. It remains relatively unchanged. I could picture John telling me about a rare green, white and gold butterfly which he told me he had seen the other day for only the second time in his life, the first time being twenty years before that.

He was a very happy man all his life, someone who took pleasure in the simple yet beautiful things that we 'townies' sometimes miss, as we live out our days in the hustle and bustle of our busy city lives. Tornagrough! I am so glad that I was introduced to the beauty of the place at a young age, and hope I will always find time to visit it and take comfort from those simple pleasures in life.

HANNAHSTOWN HILL
Gerry Turner

It was the early seventies and Seamus and I acted out our romance against the backdrop of the early 'Troubles'. This, however, did little to impede the path of true love and there were, indeed, many occasions when it added that little something. All those armoured cars, tanks and jeeps gracing the roads didn't impress me because I had my own vehicle – my lovemobile – a blue Mini, whose registration was GSF639D. As I saw it, 'G' was for Gerry, 'S' for Seamus, and 'F' for Forever – proof that we were meant for each other!

We went everywhere in that little car: me calling for him, me leaving him home, me driving and him sitting back, directing. The pattern of our life together was being established though I didn't realise it then and, to be honest, I wasn't at all unhappy with the set-up. I was looking at life through rose-tinted glasses and any feminist streak I had was being whittled away by Seamus's humour washed down with the odd vodka!

So it was that, one evening in 1973, I set off in the Mini and, per routine, I called for Seamus. He stepped out, 'tasty' as ever, and I drove us to a local bar (that night it was the Suffolk Inn). Despite the war raging round us we laughed, we sang, we drank and the craic was mighty!

The top local news item of that particular day was the disappearance of Tommy Herron, a UDA leader in

East Belfast. I recalled having seen him standing outside his headquarters on the Newtownards Road alongside his big Alsatian dog. As we drove past a shiver had gone up my spine – he was a formidable character, striking terror in people's hearts and minds, so I don't think too many people cared whether he was or wasn't found, myself included. Besides which, on that September evening, my mind was on other things and love was in the air!

As the bar closed we staggered happily out and I drove to our favourite courting spot on Hannahstown Hill – not everyone's idea of a romantic location, but then I was still wearing those rose tinted glasses! Reversing into the layby enabled us to look out over Belfast in all its splendour. The city spread out in front of us, a jewelled landscape of twinkling, sparkling lights round the deep, dark lough in the distance – a fairyland belying the hatred and evil hidden in the shadows. It was a beautiful evening and life was good!

After a time Seamus got out of the car to answer the call of nature. I put my head back, closed my eyes and sighed contentedly. However my reverie was short-lived because Seamus returned rather quickly, agitated and stuttering.

'F--- me, I think I've found Tommy Herron!'

Whilst walking round the back of the car he had inadvertently kicked at a black bag and was horrified to feel the shape of a leg. Upon hearing this my heart nearly stopped and I swore. My mind went into overdrive with thoughts of the police and the army, not forgetting my mother, the papers and my job. At no time did I feel any concern for the dead Tommy Herron lying at the back of my car. Instead, what was of utmost concern was what my mother would say about me being up Hannahstown Hill (which thought reduced a twenty-four-year-old woman to a child again!). I also worried about the effect of newspaper reports on my professional reputation: what about my colleagues, the parents, and the Board of Governors? Seamus's immediate reaction, on the other hand, was simple. 'Just drive off,' he said.

Whilst I had had no previous dealings with the police, my brain suddenly thought I had a PhD in Forensics: tyre tracks, anything we had dropped at the scene, like cigarette butts, and any potential witnesses who might place us there. The police might think we were guilty or they might just pin it on us – sure weren't there plenty such stories of people being fitted up for crimes they hadn't committed? The more Seamus said 'just drive', the more I thought of my mother, my job and the papers! We would probably have sat all night arguing the case until Seamus – against my argument that he was only adding more evidence to the crime scene – decided to go have another look at the offending black bag!!

I wrung my hands in prayer and beseeched heaven for help. Lo and behold, I was rewarded with the miraculous words, 'It was just a big dog!' Seamus was now laughing loudly but I was not placated so easily as my pessimistic nature kicked in, with the new possibility of it being Tommy Herron's Alsatian. Seamus was adamant we were leaving and dismissed my new concern, proclaiming himself indifferent and, if caught, he'd just plead manslaughter – or rather dog slaughter!

So it was that we hastily left Hannahstown Hill, now no longer a venue for our courting trysts. Tommy Herron was subsequently found shot dead in a ditch somewhere else. The whereabouts of the Alsatian continued to be a mystery and became another cold case in the history of the Troubles. For us the event was something else: a favourite in our bank of memories and ever after, when Hannahstown Hill was mentioned, Seamus and I would look at each other and say, 'Do you remember the night we found Tommy Herron there?'

TO BELONG
Abigail Bester

As a foreigner there is always the worry that you will not fit, because you are different and nobody would accept you! Moving is tough but in my case it was done for the better. I moved from the sweltering hot streets of Johannesburg, South Africa, to the beautiful rolling hills of Belfast, Northern Ireland. Dundonald's countryside is a peaceful, friendly environment where I have felt very accepted, which really made me feel at home. The bright blue sky contrasts beautifully with the bold green fields to create a vivid colour contrast which lights up this place, creating these surroundings. To belong to a city is to feel welcomed, and this is one of many great things Dundonald has to offer. The rain falls constantly which brings a sad, dull gloom over this place, but the beautiful days make up for it eventually.

Dundonald is like looking at a place on a postcard full of beauty and wonder. It is a lovely place and I thoroughly enjoy living in such a wonderful area with lovely, welcoming people. This is my home!

AS A MATTER OF FACT
Solomon Trimble

I live in a house. Most people live in a house. In fact it would be very sad if one didn't live in a house, though this is the case for many today, in our sad, unhappy world. But that is not what this piece is about. So where is this house then? It's on a hill, I guess, in a street like most city houses but once again, that not what this piece is about. So where would I find this street? It's in a town on the edge of a city, near to a rather politically biased housing estate, not uncommon to this part of the city. Yet on the other side of the city there are estates with completely opposite views. This inevitably causes problems. Riots, protests, fights and troubles. It has almost become a characteristic of the city. My city. This is what this piece is about.

I like my city. Although one day I'm planning to move, I like my city. Firstly, for the great education; this provides a lot of things – learning, friends and a sense of routine. Secondly, two-thirds of my family live here, and let's be honest, all of us love our families! Anyway, I don't have any plans for living without them while I'm under 18! Thirdly, it's my home. While this is a vague stereotypical comment, it's true! I live here. I belong here. Even amongst all the troubles and chaos, I come from here. This is my home.

LIST OF CONTRIBUTORS

Mario Abbatiello practises Reiki and counselling, and is the founder of Spiral Journey Healing Arts. His poetry has been published in several anthologies; he is also the author of *Mystery & Wonder, Maxwelton Road* and *Chicken Soup and Other Poems.*

Julie Agnew lives in Portstewart, and is studying to be a classroom assistant. She is a member of the Flowerfield Writers' Group.

Kathryn Baird trained in Classics, Greek, and Byzantine Studies. She has worked for the BBC in Belfast and London, and has translated a children's novel for the Greek publisher Psychogios.

Abigail Bester was born in South Africa, and moved to Northern Ireland in 2008. She enjoys music and English, and is a pupil at Strathearn School.

Toni Bradley has worked for many years in education, both as a teacher and as an advisor. Now semi-retired, she is a member of the Flowerfield Writers' Group.

Pauline Brady was born in the Oldpark area of Belfast. She is a teacher at the CBS Secondary School. She is part of a writing group at the Falls Women's Centre in Belfast.

Laura Cameron is a poet and founder of The Dead Shy Poets' Society. Her work has been published in printed anthologies and online journals. Her poem 'Buongiorno' was recently long-listed for the Seamus Heaney Award for New Writing.

Ciaran Carson is a poet and former Director of the Seamus Heaney Centre for Poetry at Queen's University Belfast. He has received many accolades for his work, including the T. S. Eliot Prize, the Irish Times Irish Literature Prize, the Cholmondeley Award, and the Forward Prize.

Stephanie Conn is a poet and former primary school teacher. She holds an MA in Creative Writing from Queen's University and was the winner of the inaugural Seamus Heaney Award for New Writing. In 2014 she received a Northern Ireland Arts Council Artists Career Enhancement Scheme award.

Angie Creighton was born and raised in Ballymurphy. She has held posts as a care worker and counsellor in Belfast, and is now part of a writing group at the Falls Women's Centre in Belfast.

Martin Cromie is a landscape writer, who took early retirement from education administration, and returned to full-time study at the Seamus Heaney Centre, Queen's

University Belfast. His completed PhD in Creative Writing is entitled *Spirit of the Stones*.

Deirdre Devine was born in Culdaff, Co. Donegal, and is a member of the Limavady Writers' Group. She has taught art in Derry, and recently published *In Applause,* her first collection of poetry.

Moyra Donaldson is a poet, editor, and creative writing facilitator. She has won the Allingham Award, the National Women's Poetry Competition and the Cuirt New Writing Award. Her most recent collection, *The Goose Tree*, was published by Liberties Press.

Eilish Fleming was born and raised in Belfast. She worked in the clothing industry, and is now part of a writing group at the Falls Women's Centre in Belfast.

Alan Gillis is a poet and Senior Lecturer in English at the University of Edinburgh. He is the author of *Irish Poetry of the 1930s* and *The Oxford Handbook of Modern Irish Poetry*, as well as four poetry collections, including his most recent, *Scapegoat*, published by Gallery Press.

Clodagh Brennan Harvey is a folklorist who has written extensively on Irish storytelling and cultural heritage. Poetry is now her focus, and she often uses motifs from Irish and other cultural traditions.

Lindsay Hodges lives in Belfast. Her poems have been published in journals, magazines and anthologies. She won the Hennessy Prize for Emerging Poetry and was recently shortlisted for the Seamus Heaney Award for New Writing.

Emma Kane holds a degree in Media Studies, and is a self-employed reflexologist in the North Coast area. She lives in Portstewart and is a member of the Flowefield Writers' Group.

Teresa Kane is the Principal of Magheralough Primary School, Trillick. She has worked as a freelance journalist for the BBC, and was a regional leader for the Pushkin Prize Creative Writing Trust. She has extensive experience in helping children to write poetry.

John Kelly began writing in 2012, after moving to Fermanagh. He has won several awards, including the Hungry Hill Poetry Prize.

Therese Kieran is a design graduate, and winner of Belfast Zoo's poetry competition. She was also runner-up in the Poetry Ireland/Trócaire poetry competition. Her work has appeared in several publications.

Christine Leckey was born and raised in Massachusetts. Apart from periods spent in Russia and Eastern Europe,

Northern Ireland has been her home for forty years.

Leon Litvack is Reader in Victorian Studies at Queen's University Belfast, and a world authority on the life and work of Charles Dickens. He is the originator of the Lottery-funded project 'Writing and Community; Ideas of Place', which served as the inspiration for this anthology. In 2015 he was the Eaton Fellow at the University of New Brunswick, where the work on this book was completed.

Naomi Litvack is an artist, who specialises in large-format, imagined landscapes. She is a graduate of the Manchester School of Art, and has also studied at the Akademie der Bildenden Künste in Munich. She is undertaking an MFA at the Belfast School of Art.

Medbh McGuckian is a poet, who has won the British National Poetry Competition, the Cheltenham Award, the Alice Hunt Bartlett prize, the Rooney Prize and the American Ireland Fund Literary Award. Her latest collection, *Blaris Moor*, was published by Gallery Press, and a new selected poems, entitled *The Unfixed Horizon*, was published by Wake Forest University Press.

Matthew McKay lives in Belfast, and loves foil fencing, writing and drumming. He is a pupil at the Royal Belfast Academical Institution.

Martelle Mc Partland is a poet, playwright, editor, script writer, arts facilitator and creative writing tutor. She has won many awards for her short stories, notably as a finalist in the Bridport Prize competition. She is a founding member, Chair and facilitator of Lough Neagh Writers.

Paul Maddern is a poet and creative writing tutor, who established the Seamus Heaney Centre Digital Archive at Queen's University. His collection *The Beachcomber's Report* was shortlisted for the Eithne and Rupert Strong Award for Best First Collection.

Norman Meharry served in the merchant navy and in tramp ships, before undertaking a teaching career for the government.

Erika Meitner is an American poet and Professor of English at Virginia Tech. In 2015 she was the Fulbright Scholar in Creative Writing at the Seamus Heaney Centre for Poetry at Queen's University Belfast. She is the author of four poetry collections, including her most recent, *Copia*, published by BOA Editions.

Mia Mouron-Adams lives in Newtownards. She is a pupil at Oakham School in Rutland, East Midlands.

Annemarie Mullan is a professional artist, and has an MA in Creative Writing from Queen's University. She facilitates poetry workshops and exhibits her ceramic sculptures in Belfast and Donegal.

Maurice Savage grew up in North Belfast. He became a paediatrician and developed the Dialysis and Kidney Transplant service for children in Northern Ireland. Now retired, his next writing project is a reflection on what he has learnt from his young patients in the course of his career.

Siobhan Scullion is a full-time teacher. Her poetry has been published in the Community Arts Partnership's anthology *Making Memories*, and in 2015 she was long-listed for the Seamus Heaney Award for New Writing.

James Simpson is a member of the Flowerfield Writers' Group. He placed second in the McManus Short Story Competition in 2013 and was long listed for RTE Penguin Ireland Competition in 2014.

Gráinne Tobin lives in Newcastle, Co Down, and is a founder-member of the Word of Mouth Poetry Collective. She has published two poetry collections, *Banjaxed* and *The Nervous Flyer's Companion,* and is currently working on a third.

Shelley Tracey is originally from South Africa, and has lived in Northern Ireland for over twenty years. She is a poet, researcher and community arts facilitator. Her writing has been published in a range of journals and magazines. In 2015 she received a Northern Ireland Arts Council Artist in the Community award.

Solomon Trimble lives in Belfast, and has a passion for music and languages. He is a pupil at the Royal Belfast Academical Institution.

Gerry Turner was born and raised in the Cavendish Street area of Belfast. She was a teacher until her retirement, and is now part of a writing group at the Falls Women's Centre in Belfast.